'You surprise

Lisa's tone was
were a man for
would be important.

One eyebrow lifted. 'Why, may I ask?'

'Nigel,' she told him. 'Nigel's a married man, with a wife and two children. Yet you threw him out of his job just to make room for me.'

'Does that make you feel bad?'

'As a matter of fact it does.'

'Then why don't you quit?'

WE HOPE you're enjoying our new addition to our Contemporary Romance series—stories which take a light-hearted look at the Zodiac and show that love can be written in the stars!

Every month you can get to know a different combination of star-crossed lovers, with one story that follows the fortunes of a hero and heroine when they embark on the romance of a lifetime with somebody born under another sign of the Zodiac. This month features a sizzling love-affair between **Cancer** and **Aries**.

To find out more fascinating facts about this month's featured star sign, turn to the back pages of this book. . .

ABOUT THIS MONTH'S AUTHOR

Stephanie Howard says, 'Like all people born on the cusp between two signs—in my case, Aries and Taurus—I'm a bit of both. The Taurean side of me loves luxury and comfort. My Arien side, like Lisa in the book, is impulsive, a sucker for challenge and endlessly optimistic. And, like her, I like a man who exudes a bit of mystery.

'No wonder Lisa is entranced by Alexander! No sign could possibly be more mysterious than intriguing, ever-changing Cancer!'

MIRACLES CAN HAPPEN

BY

STEPHANIE HOWARD

MILLS & BOON LIMITED
ETON HOUSE   18–24 PARADISE ROAD
RICHMOND   SURREY   TW9 1SR

*First published in Great Britain 1992
by Mills & Boon Limited*

© Stephanie Howard 1992

*Australian copyright 1992
Philippine copyright 1992
This edition 1992*

ISBN 0 263 77581 X

STARSIGN ROMANCES is a trademark of Harlequin Enterprises B.V., Fribourg Branch. Mills and Boon is an authorised user.

*Set in 10 on 12 pt Linotron Times
01-9206-48752Z
Typeset in Great Britain by Centracet, Cambridge
Made and printed in Great Britain*

CHAPTER ONE

NONE of it would have happened if it hadn't been for the dog.

It darted out in front of her, as sudden as quicksilver, as Lisa was driving her rusty old Mini towards the exit of the sunlit hotel car park. And the only way she could possibly avoid it was by swerving blindly in the opposite direction, while at the same time slamming down hard on the brake.

And that was when she hit a wet patch on the tarmac and felt the car go out of control. The next instant, as she grappled with the steering-wheel, she was thrown violently against the driver's window and there was a sickening sound of tearing metal as her offside bumper made ear-splitting contact with the side of an enormous sleek black Bentley.

Lisa felt her stomach turn over wretchedly inside her. 'As though I didn't have enough on my plate as it is!'

But at least there was one small consolation. Tail aloft and wagging in the early autumn sunshine, the dog trotted from the car park, quite unharmed.

With a sigh Lisa slumped back in her seat and pushed shaky fingers through her gold-blonde hair. 'Damn! Damn! Damn!' she muttered to herself furiously. Why did this have to happen *now*, when she was in such a hurry to get back for Emily?

But first things first. So far she hadn't dared to look directly at the Bentley. Quite frankly, she was terrified of what she might see. That crunch had sounded as though she'd ripped the door off!

Lisa took a deep breath, crossing her fingers— perhaps it had sounded worse than it was!—and forced her eyes to slide round towards the Bentley. But, at the sight that met her gaze, she snapped her eyes shut and felt her stomach turn to lead.

To her horror it was every bit as bad as she'd feared, and possibly even a tiny bit worse. There was a hideous dent in the front passenger door and the once immaculate wing was dented and scratched.

For a moment she went quite numb. This was a disaster! The owner would kill her when he saw it!

She took another deep breath and glanced at her watch, her thoughts returning with a prick of concern to Emily and her imminent dental appointment. If she went straight home now she would make it just in time to pick up her little daughter from her next-door neighbour's and escort her personally to her appointment. But if she had to start looking for the owner of the Bentley who, she guessed, was probably somewhere in the hotel, she didn't have a hope of making it in time.

Lisa hesitated for a moment, then in a flash the solution came to her. What she would do was write a note of apology, giving her name and address and telephone number, and secure it behind one of the Bentley's windscreen wipers. Then, when the owner returned, he would know who was responsible, and as soon as he contacted her she'd be only too happy to provide him with details of the accident.

But first she ought to move her car. It was blocking access to the car park exit. Gingerly she backed the old Mini away from the Bentley, then pushed the gear lever into first and began to drive forward a couple of feet.

She had barely moved an inch when she was aware of the sound of footsteps. Suddenly a tall, broad-shouldered man was standing in her path, arms extended, glowering down at her with all the wrath of hell.

'Stop right there!' He thundered the command at her. From beneath hostile dark brows a pair of black eyes bored into her. 'I'm afraid you're going nowhere, young lady!'

He was dressed in a dark suit, expensively tailored, and a plain white shirt and bright silk tie that set off the crisp, glossy blackness of his hair. And there was something about him, an aura of confidence and power, as he stood there facing her across the bonnet of the Mini that told her that even if she'd been driving a tank there was no way in the world he would have let her go past.

Lisa pushed open the driver's door and stepped out to face him. Suddenly she felt nervous, though she fought not to show it. This man looked as though he might demolish her!

She cleared her throat. 'Are you the owner of the Bentley?'

It was an unnecessary question. That he was was quite obvious. The man did not answer. He simply glared at her. 'Where did you think you were going?' he demanded.

'Nowhere. I——' She paused, meeting his look of menace. 'If you'll just give me a chance, I'll explain what I was doing. I was——'

But she got no further. The stranger stepped towards her, his face a harsh dark mask of anger. 'There's no need to explain. I know what you were doing. Not to put too fine a point on it, you were making your escape!'

'I was doing nothing of the sort! I was just moving out of the way. I was about to write you a note and stick it on your windscreen. I——'

'Hah!' he scoffed. 'Do you expect me to believe that? What you were doing was heading for the exit!'

'I wasn't heading for the exit! I was going to write you a note——'

'Yes, I heard you the first time. You were going to stick it on my windscreen.' The stranger smiled without humour. 'But I do not believe you—and I am unlikely to be won over by repetition. Remember,' he advised her, his tone like rough metal, 'I saw you—heading for the exit.'

'You saw no such thing!'

'Then perhaps my eyes deceived me? Perhaps you were travelling in the opposite direction?'

The man was impossible! Why was he accusing her? Why was he insisting that her behaviour had been dishonourable?

Lisa pulled herself up to her full five feet three inches, wishing for an extra foot or so so that she could look him in the eye. She pushed back her slim shoulders beneath the red jacket she was wearing and thrust her chin at him defiantly.

'I wasn't running away. I don't run away from my responsibilities!' And nor, she might have added, did she run away from a fight. She lacked none of the courage typical of her Aries star sign. So he could bully her all he liked. She would not let him trample over her!

She narrowed her blue eyes at him. 'What happened was this: a dog ran out in front of me as I was leaving the car park, and I had to swerve in order to avoid it. I'm sorry that in the process I hit your car, but it was an accident and, as I say——'

But he did not wait for her to finish. Arrogantly he cut in. 'So, at least you don't deny that you are responsible for the damage to my car?'

'Of course I don't deny it! What do you take me for? Why should I lie about it? I've told you it was an accident!'

As she looked up into his face Lisa was aware of eyes as black as ebony and as cold as the sea bed. For an instant she let her gaze travel over his features, highlighted for an instant in a shaft of autumn sunlight. And what she saw was a set of strong forceful lines—curved nose, high cheekbones, wide mobile mouth, a strong jutting chin and an implacable jawline.

It was a powerful face. It might even have been handsome had it not been for the dark scowl that currently shadowed it.

She took a step back. 'Look, I'm sorry about the accident. Let me give you my particulars. I'm in a terrible hurry.' She reached into the Mini and lifted out her bag and began to rummage for a pen and paper. 'As I said, I accept full responsibility for the accident. But, don't worry,' she assured him, glancing up, 'my insurance company will pay for the damage.'

Black eyes looked right through her. 'No doubt they will. However, I fear. . .' He paused a beat before continuing. 'I fear,' he went on, his tone like ice-water, 'that this incident is destined to involve more than just our insurance companies. It seems to me that this is a matter for the police.'

Lisa blinked up at him, for a moment wondering if he was joking, but there was not a shadow of humour in the dark eyes that met her own. 'Police?' she echoed disbelievingly. 'What reason could you possibly have for wanting to involve the police?'

The man straightened slightly and Lisa could sense the tautening of powerful muscles across his broad shoulders. He said, his tone measured and heavy with menace, 'I believe that, when someone deliberately inflicts damage, it is a matter for the police.'

Lisa suddenly had the sensation of being caught up in some kind of nightmare. An icy chill went through her as she looked up into his face, and she forced herself to answer calmly, 'What on earth are you talking about? Deliberate damage? I've already told you it was an accident.'

'I'm quite well aware of what you've already told me.' The line of his mouth tightened. His eyes raked her face. Then, unexpectedly, he demanded, 'What were you doing in this car park? Did you have business at the hotel?'

Lisa felt herself flush. 'No, as a matter of fact, I didn't.'

But, before she could explain, he cut in and put to her, 'I take it you are aware that this is a private car park, intended for the sole use of patrons of the hotel?'

'Yes, I'm aware of that.'

'So,' he accused her, 'what were you doing here when you had no business at the hotel?'

He was so damned arrogant! From the way he was looking at her, you'd think the damned car park, and the hotel, belonged to him!

Lisa struggled to control her annoyance as she told him, 'I know that, strictly speaking, I shouldn't have parked here. But there were loads of spaces and I also happen to know that if you don't stay long the hotel management doesn't mind.' She eyed him. 'Evidently you're a stranger around here or you'd already be aware of that fact.'

He neither confirmed nor denied that he was a stranger. Lisa sensed he considered that was none of her business.

She continued, 'I parked here because I was in a hurry. I had an extremely important appointment in town and I couldn't find a parking space anywhere else.'

She might have been speaking to him backwards in Swahili for all the attention he paid her explanation.

'So, you were parked here illegally,' he insisted without a flicker, 'and I caught you trying to sneak back out again, after having inflicted considerable damage to my car. If you ask me, that adds up to a highly questionable scenario.'

'And, if you ask me, you're the victim of a paranoid imagination! You're suggesting that I damaged your car deliberately. Why on earth would I want to do a thing like that?'

He smiled a harsh smile. 'You tell me,' he invited.

'I'm afraid I have absolutely no idea. I don't even know you, so I'm hardly likely to be harbouring some secret grudge against you!'

Deliberately she looked him in the eye as she said it. Though I can easily understand, her gaze told him plainly, the reason for your evident paranoia. There must be no shortage of people who hold grudges against you if your current display of arrogance is anything to go by.

She tossed her gold-blonde head and added levelly, 'And I'm not some kind of vandal, if that's what you're suggesting.'

'I never thought you were.' His gazed pierced through her. Then he paused before demanding, 'Answer me this. . .if it was an accident and you're not a vandal, but rather, as you would clearly have me believe, an honest, decent, upright citizen, why did you try to sneak away? Why didn't you come and report the damage to me? You must have guessed I'd be somewhere in the hotel.'

He held her gaze a moment, one hostile eyebrow lifting. 'In my book, that's the sort of response to be expected of an honest, decent, upright citizen.'

And it was precisely what in normal circumstances Lisa would have done. She took a deep breath. 'Look, I was in a hurry. It's my little girl. She has a dental appointment this afternoon and she's been a little bit nervous about it. My next-door neighbour agreed to take her, but I promised I'd do my best to get back in time so that I could take her myself.'

Her eyes flickered defiantly. 'Believe it or not, my responsibility to my daughter rated higher in my mind than going to seek you out at the hotel.' Then she added quickly, lest he deliberately misinterpret that, 'But I was going to leave you a note, as I keep trying to tell you. I thought that would be a perfectly adequate compromise in the circumstances.'

He had listened to her in silence, but now he smiled a cynical smile. 'That's a very touching story, but it'll take a little more than that to convince me that you weren't heading for the exit.'

The man was infuriating! Why wouldn't he believe her? Did she look like a criminal or something?

Lisa watched as he stepped past her to examine the Bentley, running long tanned fingers across the scratched and dented surface. 'Have you any idea what this will cost to repair?' He threw her an angry look over his shoulder. 'My guess is at least a couple of thousand.'

Lisa felt her stomach twist uncomfortably inside her. A couple of thousand was considerably more than her own car was worth! And she was aware that the same thought had occurred to him as he observed, 'If your own car has suffered any damage in the incident, I'm afraid it's rather hard to identify. It looks as though it's been in a few scrapes before.'

Lisa pulled a face. 'One or two.' The car was old. She'd had it for seven years, and it had been a few years old when she and Tony had bought it. A couple of winters ago, caught out on a patch of ice, she'd had a mild argument with a lamppost, damaging more or less the same spot that had been damaged again today. She'd been planning to have it repaired as soon as she could afford to, for, although she knew she could have claimed the cost through her insurance, she couldn't afford to lose her no-claims bonus. Money really was that tight.

Well, she'd lost her bonus now, she observed ruefully to herself as the tall dark stranger turned once more to look at her and remarked in a scathing tone of voice, 'I would say that, considering the state your car's in, about the only thing it's good for is to be used as a battering-ram.'

That annoyed her. Lisa's blue eyes flashed at him indignantly. 'It may seem so to you, but you can take my word for it, if I were in the business of prowling around car parks looking for innocent Bentleys to wreck, I most certainly wouldn't use my own car as a battering-ram. I'm far too fond of it for that. What I'd do is keep a handy sledge-hammer in the boot!'

'I doubt you could fit a sledge-hammer into a Mini's boot.'

As he said it for the first time a smile flickered across his face, and in that instant his features were totally transformed. The harshness vanished, as though a dark veil had been lifted. For one fleeting moment the dark eyes seemed to dance.

In spite of herself, Lisa smiled back in response. So there was more to him than mere harshness and arrogance. Perhaps not a great deal, but at least a glimmer! She nodded in agreement. 'It would be a bit of a struggle.'

He held her gaze a moment, still with a ghost of a smile lingering. 'I think, after all, what you probably are is a perfectly respectable wife and mother, and that all you're guilty of is a momentary lapse.'

So, he had taken her earlier reference to her daughter Emily to mean that there was a husband in her life as well. There had been once, but that was not his business. It was not necessary for him to know that she'd been a widow for years.

She finished scribbling her details on the back of the old envelope that she had extricated from her bag. Handing it to him, she told him, 'My name and address are on the front. And now perhaps you would be good enough to give me your particulars?'

'Certainly.' He reached into his inside jacket pocket, drew out a fine black leather wallet, flicked it open and with his long tanned fingers slid out a printed business card. Replacing the wallet, he produced a gold pen, scribbled quickly on the back of it and handed it to Lisa.

'I hope you'll still be in time for your daughter's dental appointment,' he told her. 'I know how traumatic visits to the dentist can be.'

Lisa took the proffered card, privately reflecting that she could not imagine this man being traumatised by anything. He was one of these people, she sensed, whom nothing touched. He had an aura about him of total immunity.

She took the card and told him, 'Oh, I've missed the

appointment. Thanks to you, my daughter will be on her way to the dentist without me.'

It had been her intention simply to pocket the card, contemptuously, without bothering to glance at it, but something in that darkly uncaring face of his sparked a flash of angry curiosity within her. Who was this monstrous man who had just inflicted on her one of the most unpleasant encounters in her entire life?

Her eyes strayed to the card that she still held in her hand and she almost started as she saw, written in plain bold print, a name that had featured with such regularity recently in the headlines of the business section of the local newspaper that she could not fail to recognise it.

Lisa glanced up at him, frowning, and heard herself ask him, 'Are you *the* Alexander Vass?'

He looked back at her unblinkingly. 'Is there more than one?'

'I suppose not——'

She paused, annoyed at her own gaucheness. The revelation of his identity had thrown her a little. This man, whose name was so familiar to her, whose company's recent comings and goings on the stock-market had been so well chronicled, and of some special interest to her, was a great deal younger than she had expected. Alexander Vass, the shipping magnate who had recently taken over the local firm of G.W. Fashions after a bitter struggle with his rivals, she had expected to be a man well into middle age, in spite of the fact that she knew him to be single. But the man who stood before her was no more than thirty-five.

And yet she had no doubts that, in spite of his youth, he was exactly who she had supposed him to be. Hadn't she sensed the shrewdness and strength of purpose that lay behind those mask-like features? One could tell he was a man who had come a long way, and who intended going a great deal further.

'So, that's why you're in Liskeard?' She threw him a half-smile. 'No doubt you've been overseeing the physical takeover of your new business?'

He did not answer. His expression was glacial. It was perfectly clear that Alexander Vass considered her remark to be a gross impertinence. Quite evidently it was not his habit to discuss his business affairs with strangers.

Lisa felt duly chastened, though her remark had been quite innocent. It had not been her intention in any way to pry. Almost apologetically, as though to make up for her *faux pas*, she offered a piece of information of her own.

'I was interested because I'm in the fashion business, too. I'm a designer,' she added when he simply looked right through her. 'Though not the sort of designer,' she permitted herself to elaborate, 'that you would be likely to employ at G.W. Fashions.'

One hostile dark eyebrow lifted briefly and a pair of diamond-hard eyes swept quickly over her, seeming to assess in the flicker of an eyelid the stylish dark red outfit she was wearing.

Lisa found herself rushing on to inform him, 'This is one of my more conservative creations.' Befitting, she added silently, my recent appointment with my bank manager! 'Normally my designs run towards the more avant-garde.'

Alexander Vass said nothing for a moment. Then in a dry tone he observed, 'In that case, you are right. The designers employed by G.W. Fashions most definitely could not be described as avant-garde.'

Lisa stifled her laughter. 'Definitely not. Quite the opposite, I would say!'

'Would you, now?' Vass smiled at her curiously. 'So, how exactly would you describe G.W. Fashions?'

Did he want the truth? Somehow Lisa doubted it. Which was probably why she decided to give it to him anyway.

She shrugged. 'In a word, I'd call them old-fashioned.'

There was a momentary silence. The dark eyes scrutinised her. 'Old-fashioned, you say? Not merely traditional?'

Had she offended him? She wasn't certain. That inscrutable face gave nothing away. But, just in case she hadn't, she decided to have another shot at it. After all the incivilities he'd been hurling at her, he deserved to be put in his place a little!

'No, I wouldn't call them traditional.' She held his eyes without a flicker. What she was offering was her honest opinion. It was simply a happy coincidence that it sounded like an insult! She smiled. 'What I would call them is fuddy-duddy.'

There was a momentary reaction at the back of his eyes, though she could not quite manage to interpret it. A brief pause followed, then he asked a question. 'So, for whom do you produce these avant-garde designs of yours? What company has the pleasure of employing you?'

'I'm self-employed.' She said it quickly, with pride, yet acknowledging to herself that it wasn't strictly accurate. She was on her own. That part of it was true enough. But she had yet to get her business started. She was still gathering together the finance she needed. Hence the meeting with her bank manager earlier this afternoon!

Alexander Vass's eyes had never left her face. 'So, you are one of my competitors?'

'No, not really. As I told you, I have my eyes on a very different sort of market. My designs aim to appeal to the style-conscious young, whereas yours are strictly for retired country ladies.' That was a slight exaggeration, but she could not resist it. 'And, besides, my business is only very tiny. A mere sprat to your colossal mackerel.'

Vass smiled a slow smile, as warm as a winter's morning. 'In that case, beware.' He paused for an instant, just long enough for her to register the warning reflected in his eyes. 'I expect you know about sprats and mackerels? The latter tend to swallow up the former.'

She had invited that, yet his arrogance stung her. Lisa swung angrily away from him and stepped towards her battered Mini. 'I think we've concluded our business,' she told him crisply as she snatched open the driver's door and climbed into the sun-warmed interior. 'Now it's up to our insurance companies to sort things out between them.'

'Indeed it is.' Vass pocketed the envelope she had

given him. 'Let's hope there are no further problems to trouble us.'

'Let's *pray* there aren't!' Lisa muttered beneath her breath as she slammed the car door shut and switched on the engine. 'And let's pray this is the last time I need ever set eyes on you!'

She was aware that he stood watching her as she set off towards the exit. She could feel the dark eyes boring into the back of her neck. But she resisted the urge to turn and glance at him and kept her eyes fixed straight ahead.

It was only as she was heading out into the road that she raised her eyes to the rear-view mirror. And it seemed to her that for a moment his eyes ensnared her, as though he had reached out a hand and taken hold of her.

In spite of the warmth of the car, she shivered.

CHAPTER TWO

'YOU worry too much.' That was what Josey had told
Lisa when she'd finally got home, flush-faced and
anxious, still upset from her angry encounter with
Alexander Vass and worried sick about little Emily.

And perhaps her friend was right, Lisa thought to
herself now as she sank back in her armchair in front
of the gas fire, put her feet up at last and took a
mouthful of her cocoa. Emily's visit to the dentist had
gone off without trauma. In fact, it had proved to be a
triumphant event.

'Look what Mr Dobson gave me!' were the first
words from the little girl as Lisa had hurried through
her next-door neighbour Josey's front door. And there
had stood Emily in the middle of the hallway, holding
aloft a shiny red apple, her pretty tomboy face
wreathed in happy smiles, not a trace of the tear-stains
Lisa had been so worried about seeing.

She had bent to hug her daughter, relief pouring
through her and mingling with the joy that always sang
in her veins whenever she held her precious bundle in
her arms. 'Clever girl!' she'd exclaimed, kissing the
child's pale blonde hair. 'And what did Mr Dobson say
about your teeth?'

'He said they were perfect. A-one perfect. And he
said I was to come back in six months' time.'

'I told you she'd be all right,' Josey had chastised

Lisa later. 'She was only upset yesterday because some silly schoolmate was telling her horror stories about visits to the dentist. You know she's never had any problems in the past.'

'I know.' Lisa had sighed and squeezed her friend's arm, reflecting for the hundred-millionth time just what an enormous debt she owed Josey.

Josey, who lived next door with her husband Charlie, had a son a year or so older than Emily. And right from day one, from the day Emily had been born, Josey had offered her services as a child-minder.

Lisa knew she could never have managed without her. Life for a single parent was never easy—struggling to cope with the demands of a new baby, while at the same time trying to hold down a job. And it could be especially hard when there was no family to help out.

That was Lisa's situation. Her family were all up north, in Darlington, right at the other end of the country. And she had no in-laws. Tony's parents lived abroad.

And then, of course, six years ago she had still been reeling from the shock of Tony's death. It had happened so suddenly. An inoperable brain tumour. It had taken her a long time to get over that.

She sighed now and wrapped her hands around her cocoa mug, letting her eyes drift to the framed photograph on top of the bookshelves. It was her wedding picture, taken almost seven years ago, a picture of two blissful nineteen-year-old faces, confidently looking forward to a future together, a future that was destined never to be.

For, less than a year after that picture had been

taken, Tony was dead and Lisa, six months pregnant, her life suddenly shattered, was on her own.

It seemed so long ago now. Lisa stared into her cocoa mug. Those few short months with Tony seemed sometimes like a dream to her. She took a mouthful of her drink. Though it was no dream, it was a part of her. And the living proof of that was Emily.

Lisa smiled to herself. Dear, precious Emily. And, instantly, her thoughts switched from the past to the future.

Josey had wanted to know all about her meeting with her bank manager. 'How did it go?' she'd demanded. 'Did you get the loan?'

Lisa had nodded, feeling excitement rush through her. 'I more or less had to prise it out of him, but in the end he decided I wasn't such a bad risk, after all.'

'Of course you're not a bad risk!' Josey had been instantly supportive. 'You're an extremely talented and original designer.' She'd grinned and tossed back her pony-tailed head. 'I just *know* you're going to make a huge success. One day you'll be up there with Ozbek and Galliano!'

Such faith! Such dreams! Lisa had flushed with pleasure. And, even now, remembering, she felt a warm glow spread through her. Josey was a friend in a million. Whenever she needed a bit of encouragement, Josey never failed her.

And she had never needed Josey's encouragement more than she had just a matter of a few short weeks ago. For she'd literally been shaken to her roots when the clothing firm she'd worked for for the past six and a half years had collapsed, making the entire work-force redundant.

What am I to do? had been her first stunned reaction. I have a child to support, a mortgage to repay!

And then, as though it had been waiting there to be born, a plan had begun to come to life in her mind. Once she had figured it all out, she had put her plan to Josey and waited to see her friend's reaction.

'I'm going to go it alone. It's what I've always wanted. With the redundancy money, pittance though it is, plus a small bank loan to help pad it out, I should just about be able to afford to rent and equip a small workshop.' She'd seized her friend excitedly by the arm. 'What do you think? Do you think I'm crazy?'

Josey's reaction had taken her a little by surprise. Lisa had known her friend would back her. Didn't she always? But she had not been prepared for the intensity of her response.

'It's right for you, Lisa. I know it's right. For far too long you've been hiding your light under a bushel. It's time to get out there and let the world see how good you are. And you'll make it, I know you will. You have the guts to do it!'

Lisa drained her cocoa mug and leaned back in her chair, smiling as she recalled their conversation. Now it was up to her to prove that Josey was right. The chance to be her own boss, to give free rein to her design flair, to stand up and reach out for the stars. . .finally that chance was hers.

Excitement buzzed through her. She just knew she could make a go of it! This opportunity to strike out for independence was precisely what her fiery Arien temperament craved!

On a bubble of elation, full of dreams for the future, Lisa switched off the gas fire and headed for bed.

She had entirely forgotten about Alexander Vass and that unfortunate collision with his Bentley.

It was only after she had packed Emily off to school next morning that, with a sudden feeling of doom, Lisa remembered. Her insurance company. She had forgotten to call them to report the accident.

She glanced at her watch. She must do it now, though she was rushing to get ready for another appointment—this time with one of the estate agents in town who had rung to tell her he had an attic to let for what sounded like a very reasonable rent. With any luck this might turn out to be the workshop she was looking for!

Lisa snatched up the phone, annoyed at her own forgetfulness. She'd fully intended to call the insurance company yesterday afternoon, as soon as she had got home. But there was no harm done. A half-day's delay hardly mattered.

The phone was answered at once. 'Put me through to the motor claims department,' Lisa requested, glancing again at her watch. This only ought to take a couple of minutes, then she could be on her way to find out more about the attic.

The girl in the claims department took her particulars. 'Just a moment,' she said, 'till I find you on the computer.'

Lisa drummed her fingers impatiently on the phone

table. 'Come on,' she was muttering under her breath. 'Get a move on! I'm in a hurry!'

But the girl seemed to leave her hanging for ages. 'Hello? Hello?' Lisa called into mouthpiece. At this rate she was going to be late for her appointment!

Then at last the girl came back to her, but, even as she began to speak, Lisa could sense an ominous note in her voice. 'I've checked and rechecked,' the girl told her, almost apologetically, 'but I'm afraid I have some rather bad news for you. . .'

Then, still in that apologetic tone of voice, she went on to strike Lisa with a thunderbolt. As Lisa laid down the phone her hand was shaking.

She stared blankly at the wall above the phone table. Surely this catastrophe couldn't really be happening?

But even as she shuddered, knowing that it was, the phone on the table began to ring.

Lisa knew who it must be. She stared at the phone sickly. Her dreams, she sensed, were collapsing into nightmare.

It took all her strength to reach out for the receiver and raise it stiffly to her ear. 'Hello?' she said. Heart beating, she waited to hear the voice that she knew she must hear.

'Mrs Howell?'

At the familiar cold tones Lisa shivered. She grasped the receiver tightly. 'Yes, this is Lisa Howell,' she answered.

'And this,' came the response, 'is Alexander Vass. No doubt you were expecting to hear from me, and no doubt you are aware of what it is I want to talk about?'

'Yes, I'm aware.' Her tone was leaden. She felt as though all the life had been punched out of her body.

'Be at my hotel in fifteen minutes' time. I'll be waiting for you in my suite.'

'But I have an appointment. Can't I come later? I'm not trying to wriggle out of it, but my appointment is important.'

'Your appointments, it would seem, are always important.' His tone was laced liberally with sarcasm. In her mind's eye Lisa could see those hostile dark eyebrows lifting magisterially as he assured her, 'But the most important appointment you have today is with me. Take my word for that, Mrs Howell. Fifteen minutes,' he reiterated sharply. 'I would advise you most sincerely not to keep me waiting.'

Lisa was inclined to believe that advice was worth following. Ten minutes later, dressed in a pair of grey trousers and the same red jacket she'd been wearing yesterday, she was turning into the hotel car park, slotting her Mini quickly into one of the spaces, then striding resolutely towards the hotel's main entrance.

What fate awaited her? She hardly dared imagine.

The girl at the reception desk nodded when she introduced herself. 'Ah, yes, Mr Vass is expecting you, Mrs Howell.' She pointed towards the lifts as she quoted Vass's suite number. 'Take the lift to the fourth floor.'

Lisa's fists were clenched tightly at her sides as she rode up to the fourth floor in the silent lift. As the doors opened she stepped out and glanced quickly round her at the tastefully lavish five-star décor. A suite here for one night would cost, she decided, a couple of weeks of her former salary.

She reached the door of his suite, knocked twice, firmly, and prepared to meet that hostile dark gaze. If he thought he could intimidate her he was gravely mistaken!

He had been waiting for her, it seemed. The door opened instantly. Dark eyes pierced through her as he stepped aside to let her enter. 'Your time-keeping, if nothing else, is perfect,' he observed drily.

Over the hours since she had last confronted him Lisa had forgotten just what an extraordinarily imposing figure he was. He was taller than she remembered, more powerfully built, the angles of his face even harder and more menacing than she had recalled coming up in the lift.

Dressed now in a sharply cut plain grey suit, his thick black hair slicked back from his forehead, he seemed to fill the room with his own visceral energy. As though the very lamps in the gleaming candelabra were powered by the electricity that seemed to radiate from his skin.

Lisa turned to face him. 'I have an explanation.'

'I'll bet you do. And I'm longing to hear it.'

'It wasn't deliberate. I never meant to lie to you. Please believe me. It was an honest mistake.'

Black eyebrows lifted, hostile and condemning. 'You mean it simply didn't cross your mind to inform me yesterday that you have no insurance?'

Lisa felt the cold finger of panic momentarily touch her, just as it had when, over the phone earlier, the girl from the claims department had told her the awful truth.

She took a deep breath. 'I didn't know I had no insurance. I didn't realise that it had run out.'

Alexander Vass delivered a scathing glance. 'Do you seriously expect me to believe that?' he challenged.

'Why shouldn't you believe it? It's the honest truth! You don't seriously think I'd drive around knowing that my insurance was out of date? That would be a pretty irresponsible thing to do!'

'I agree entirely. Irresponsible and foolish. Not to mention financially reckless.' He paused an instant, his eyes without mercy. 'I received an estimate for repairs to my car last night. It seems it's going to cost you over three and half thousand pounds.'

Lisa very nearly fainted. She felt the room recede sharply then start to whirl around her head. She blinked and clenched her fists, struggling for control. 'You can't be serious!' she protested.

But he was. 'Repairs to Bentley Continentals are notoriously expensive, alas, especially when they involve major damage to the bodywork. The door you dented will have to be replaced and the damaged bumper straightened and resprayed.'

'But I can't pay it! I don't have that kind of money!' The protest issued from her lips like a cry of despair. 'I'll be ruined if I have to pay!'

'You ought to have thought of that before you drove into my car. I hate to sound callous, but you brought this on yourself.'

Lisa almost laughed at that. So, he hated to sound

callous? She suspected the opposite, that he was rather enoying it.

As she stood there, swaying slightly, her cheeks as pale as parchment, she was aware that Vass was gesturing towards the sofa and inviting her in a tone of mock-concern, 'Why don't you take a seat? You look a little shaken. Perhaps I ought to fix you a drink?'

'I don't need a drink,' she muttered through clenched teeth. Damn him and his air of condescension! But she was reluctantly grateful to accept his invitation to take a seat. Her legs had turned to powder. They could scarcely hold her.

'Perhaps a coffee would be in order?' As she slumped against the sofa cushions Vass reached for the phone and dialled for room service. 'A strong black coffee, that's what you need.'

Feeling a little better now that the weight was off her feet and the room had finally stopped swimming around her, Lisa watched him through lowered lashes as he phoned down his order.

Three and a half thousand pounds was a nightmare figure. If he forced her to pay it now it really would ruin her. But perhaps he would not force her. Perhaps he would be lenient. After all, he was an immensely wealthy man. The head of Silver Star Navigation. A millionaire many times over. He was surely in no great hurry for the money.

And besides, it occurred to her, her eyes narrowing as she continued to watch him, there was something different about him today, some quality that had definitely not been there yesterday, and that in her initial agitation had eluded her till now.

She would not have gone so far as to define it as softness. Softness and this man Vass definitely did not go together! It was more a lightness of humour that shone through his anger. He seemed less of the dictator than he had appeared to her yesterday!

From this slimly positive sign she instantly gathered optimism, as it was her nature to do, and, forcing aside despair, proceeded to concentrate on the only course of action, she sensed, that could save her.

She must win him round. She must persuade him of her good intentions—for it had never crossed her mind that she would not repay him—but she must also try to convince him of the seriousness of her situation and persuade him to grant her a bit of leeway. And, in order to do that, she must be sympathetic!

By the time he had finished ordering coffee, and, laying down the phone, was turning towards her, Lisa was sitting upright in her seat, her blue eyes alert and perfectly focused.

'You're really very kind.' She forced herself to smile at him. 'A coffee is exactly what I need. To someone like myself the sum you mentioned is an enormous amount of money.' She paused and cast a meaningful glance round the room, whose size and furnishings had caused her to double her original estimate. His suite would probably cost nearer four weeks' salary than two.

She kept the smile pinned to her face. 'I suppose to you that sounds funny?'

'That you should consider three and a half thousand pounds a lot of money?' His eyes skimmed her face, his expression unreadable, as he seated himself in the armchair opposite her. He stretched out his legs and let his gaze mesh with hers. 'No, I don't find that funny in the slightest. I, too, think it's rather a lot of money.'

Was he calling her bluff or was he serious? Lisa had absolutely no way of knowing. Vass, she was fast learning, was a hard man to figure out.

She sat forward in her seat. 'About this insurance business. . .Perhaps I should explain my situation. . .Then at least you can appreciate how it came about.'

Vass flicked her a crushing look from beneath hostile eyebrows. 'I don't really think I'm interested in knowing such details. All I'm really interested in is receiving your cheque for my repair bill.'

Had she been wrong, after all, Lisa suddenly wondered, about that underlying lightness of mood she had sensed in him? She regarded him squarely. One way or the other, the task she had set herself was not going to be easy!

She said, keeping the smile fixed firmly on her face, 'Perhaps, once you've heard my story, you'll feel a little differently. I really do have a very good excuse.'

'No doubt you do.' His eyes bored through her. 'After all, you've had all night to think of one.'

Lisa's smile slipped then. 'That's not fair!' she protested. 'Why are you always accusing me of dishonesty?'

'I wonder.' He smiled cynically and spread his fingers across the chair arms, the tan of his skin dark and vivid against the blue silk. 'I wonder where on earth I could have got the idea that you are a dishonest, lying, cheating young woman? Personally, I can't even begin to imagine.'

Lisa felt like slapping him for his sarcasm and his arrogance. But she restrained herself and, instead, retaliated verbally, abandoning for the moment her attempt to be sympathetic.

'If I may say so,' she told him, 'you appear to be a man with a weakness for making judgements on very little evidence.'

She felt pleased with her choice of words. Her use of 'weakness' sounded belittling, precisely the effect that she had been aiming for. She continued, 'I would have thought that for a man in your position, required to make countless decisions every day, such a weakness would prove to be a considerable handicap.'

Inwardly she smiled. That was another good choice of words. Handicaps, like weaknesses, she sensed instinctively, would not be part of Alexander Vass's self-image.

He smiled, surprising her. So she had been right about his mood! Yesterday, she felt certain, he would not have been amused!

'Mrs Howell, I confess I have many weaknesses. . .' As he said it he let his hands caress the silk chair-arms, the movement seeming to echo the drift of his dark eyes as, unhurriedly, and with appreciation, they surveyed her. 'Although none of them,' he added, 'has so far proved to be a handicap. I manage to function exceedingly well.'

In an instant, without touching her, he had stripped her naked. Lisa felt her flesh burn beneath the bold gaze. And for a moment she was thrown. Suddenly she saw him in a new guise. As a man of intense and disturbing sexuality.

His gaze returned to her face, as though nothing had happened. 'But I take your point. So far I have seen only your bad side. Perhaps there is another side worth considering.' His eyebrows lifted inquisitorially. 'Go ahead. Try to convince me.'

So, at least, she was being offered a chance to state her case! Lisa took a deep breath and crossed her slim trousered legs. 'Let me explain first about the insurance,' she began. 'It was due for renewal yesterday, but I entirely forgot about it. You see, I've had rather a lot on my mind recently. . .'

His smile parodied sympathy. 'Don't we all, Mrs Howell?' Then the dark eyebrows once more lifted. 'Please continue,' he bade her.

Lisa ignored the caustic comment. 'You see,' she told him, 'I lost my job. The company I worked for folded just a couple of weeks ago.'

He pounced on that instantly. 'I thought you told me yesterday you were self-employed?'

'I know.' She hurried on before he could accuse her again of lying. 'I'm planning to be. I'm working on it. I've got the finance I need and I may have found premises.' As she said it her expression lit up with enthusiasm. 'With any luck, I'll be in business before the month's out.'

But she was digressing. She pulled herself back to the point, assuming once more an expression of sobriety. 'The past two weeks have been pretty scary. Setting up one's own business is a pretty big enterprise, and I've a five-year-old daughter whose welfare I have to consider.'

'So why didn't you just look for another job, instead of involving yourself in such a risky undertaking?'

'Because I want to work for myself. I want to be independent. And besides,' she added on a note of practicality, sensing that he was unlikely to be moved by her ambitions, 'there aren't many jobs around in Cornwall for fashion designers.'

'What about G.W. Fashions? Did you try us?'

'No.' She looked back at him. Hadn't he understood that she wasn't interested in working for anybody else? 'But one of my ex-workmates did,' she informed him truthfully. 'She was told there weren't any vacancies. But she was lucky in the end. She's been offered a job in London.'

Vass nodded. 'Yes, London is undoubtedly the best place to go to find a job in the fashion industry.' The dark eyes narrowed. He scrutinised her for a moment. 'Too bad that option's not open to you. I expect you're tied here by your husband's job?'

Lisa blinked at him, and then she remembered. Yesterday, in the course of their confrontation in the car park, he had assumed she was married and she had not corrected him.

She looked back at him now, at the handsome, sculpted face, and was aware of a sudden inexplicable urge to let him go on believing that she was married. She would feel safer behind the shield of a make-believe husband.

But that was a crazy thought! Where had it come from? She needed no shields against Alexander Vass!

Quickly she assured him. 'I have no husband, Mr Vass. My husband is dead. I'm a widow.'

He glanced at her left hand. 'You wear a wedding-ring.'

'Is there some reason why I shouldn't?' Lisa snapped the question at him. Surely he wasn't accusing her of lying about this, too?

He ignored her outraged question. 'Is your widow-hood recent?' His tone was soft, falsely respectful. 'If it is, please accept my deepest sympathy.'

His sympathy, Lisa judged, was probably worth about as much as the dirt beneath his fingernails—that is, if there had been a speck of dirt present beneath those immaculately manicured items!

She rejected his false offering and informed him coolly, 'I've been a widow for many years. And, since you're so interested, the reason I wear my wedding-ring is strictly for the sake of appearances. I have a daughter, remember.'

She glanced down at the ring now, and found herself wondering, as she did occasionally, if it really was necessary for her to go on wearing it. Everyone knew that she and Tony had been married. And that part of her life seemed like such a long time ago.

But, even as she thought it, she rejected the question and felt a surge of anger go darting through her. How dared this man, a virtual stranger, stir up these doubts in so private an area of her life?

She flicked him a cool look. 'So, now you know. Now you know why my insurance was out of date. I happen to have a great deal on my mind at the moment.

Starting up a business, when you're a complete beginner, as I said, is a rather daunting affair.'

'So, why do it? Why don't you follow in your workmate's footsteps and find yourself a salaried job in London?'

Lisa bit back her annoyance. Why was he so determined to deny her the right to reach for her dream?

In a carefully measured tone she pointed out to him, 'I couldn't afford to live in London. London house prices are way beyond my reach. And, besides, my daughter's school is here, and all her friends. I'd take a local job, doing anything, before I'd uproot her.'

She meant that. She had thought about it in the dark hours of the night. In the event, heaven forbid, that her business should not succeed, she would indeed take the first local job she was offered.

But that was not the issue now and it was none of Vass's business. She smiled a little brittlely and returned to the subject in question. 'Perhaps now you can appreciate my dilemma—about paying for the damage to your car?'

'Indeed I can.' His eyes were unreadable. 'I can appreciate that that will pose a considerable problem.'

That did not sound promising. Lisa felt her mouth go dry. 'I'm afraid it's worse that that,' she answered, frowning. 'I'm afraid there's no way I can possibly pay it at the moment.'

'But it has to be paid, and it has to be paid now.'

'I would pay it if I could.'

'You have no choice but to pay it. On your own admission you are totally liable.'

'Yes, I don't deny that.' As Lisa held the stone-hard

gaze her heart was clattering. All at once she was sweating ice. 'But I can't pay you at the moment. I'd need a little time. I'm really sorry. It's just impossible.'

'What about the money you plan to use for your business?' As her heart stopped inside her he continued mercilessly, 'Surely you could use that to pay me?'

That idea had occurred to Lisa, but she had discarded it as unthinkable. To hear it on his lips now sent a dart of terror through her.

'You wouldn't! Surely you wouldn't take that money away from me? It's all I have! I'd be left with nothing!' Suddenly every inch of her was tight and trembling. 'That money is for my future and for the future of my little girl!'

'That is unfortunate.' The dark eyebrows lowered threateningly. 'But debts, I'm afraid, have to be paid.'

He really meant it. He would ruin her without flinching. Lisa felt her stomach turn over sickly inside her. She could see her future closing like a fist before her eyes.

She felt like weeping. Without shame, she pleaded, 'Please, Mr Vass. Please don't do it! Have a little mercy. Anything but that!'

'Anything?' He smiled and leaned towards her. The dark eyes slid over her, just as they had earlier, seeming to strip the clothes from her skin.

Then he sat back in his chair again. 'Since you declare yourself so amenable, as a matter of fact, I have a proposition.'

CHAPTER THREE

AT THAT precise moment there was a knock on the door.

'That must be room service with our coffee.' As Lisa stared back at him, numb and rigid, from the sofa, Alexander Vass rose swiftly to his feet and on long strides crossed to open the door.

Lisa watched in a kind of mute subdued horror as the waiter came in and began to arrange the coffee things on a low glass-topped table between Vass's armchair and her sofa.

She hardly dared glance at Alexander Vass. That word 'proposition' and the look of appraisal that had accompanied it, when she recalled them, still sent shivers through her. What had he understood when she'd pleaded 'Anything but that'? Had he understood that in her desperation to avert financial tragedy she might be willing to barter her body?

If he had, she thought, appalled, he'd understood wrongly! Desperate she might be, but not as desperate as that!

The waiter had retreated now, leaving them alone, and Vass had seated himself once more opposite her and was proceeding to take charge of the pouring of the coffee.

He glanced across at her, his dark eyes seeming to

linger. 'How do you like your coffee? Black or white? With sugar?'

It seemed to Lisa, in her state of heightened sensitivity, that there was a touch of intimacy in the way he asked those simple questions, as though this proposition of his, which she felt surer by the minute involved some basic sexual exchange, had already been spelled out, and, what was more, accepted. Any minute and he would be inviting her through to the bedroom and urging her to call him Alexander!

Her tone was clipped as she answered, 'White, with sugar. And, by the way, Mr Vass, let's get one thing straight——'

'Call me Alexander. Don't let's stand on formality.' As Lisa stuttered to a halt—had he read her mind or something?—he added, 'After all, we're not exactly strangers any more.'

Or won't be very soon. Was that what he was implying? Lisa felt herself spring forward. 'Look, Mr Vass——'

But he cut through her protest. 'You said white with sugar. I suppose with that lovely slim figure of yours you don't have to worry about the calories.' He smiled. 'I'm the same. I just seem to burn them off.'

Was that supposed to be some kind of sexual allusion? Were his words intended to fire her imagination with racy images of the two of them burning up calories together between a pair of scented sheets?

The thought, accompanied by just such an image, jumped into Lisa's head before she could stop it. She thrust it back out again and scowled across at him as, with a smile, he handed her her coffee-cup.

'As I was saying, Mr Vass. . .About that proposition of yours. . .Please don't get the wrong idea. I have no intention whatsoever of. . .'

As she paused momentarily, pillaging her brain for a discreet way of expressing what was essentially indiscreet, he cut in again. 'As I see it, Lisa, you don't really have a great deal of room for manoeuvre. You're in a tight spot. If you refuse to co-operate I can force you to pay me the money you owe me. And I'm prepared to do it. I'm quite prepared to sue you.'

'For three and a half thousand pounds?' The threat served to anger her. 'Would you really, a man of your enormous wealth, sue someone like me for a sum that to you is little more than pocket-money, but to me represents my very livelihood? Would you really,' she flung at him, 'sink as low as that?'

'You might be surprised at how low I'm prepared to sink.' Without batting an eyelid, Vass helped himself to sugar. 'Not that I think there's anything to be ashamed of in pursuing one's legitimate debts. One does not succeed in business,' he added with a dry smile, 'by treating three and a half thousand pounds as pocket-money.'

OK, so perhaps she'd been pushing it a little! Lisa bit her lip. 'I was simply making a point. To part with that money at this moment would wipe out my future. It would ruin me completely.'

Then she hurried on before he could interrupt her, 'Let me repay you later, once I've got my business started, once I've managed to get on my feet. I'll even pay you interest,' she added recklessly. Anything to make him bite!

Alexander Vass leaned back in his chair and took a slow sip of his coffee. 'An interesting offer.' He seemed to consider. 'But one, I must confess, that has limited appeal.'

'Why? I told you I'd pay you interest. There's no way that you could lose!'

'That's your opinion.' His eyes locked with hers. Unhurriedly he leaned forward to lay his cup back on the table. Then he leaned back again, resting his dark head against the chair back. 'And I assure you I'm impressed by your confidence in your own abilities. But, alas, as ungenerous as this may sound, I find myself unable to share that confidence. . .' He smiled a slow smile and pointed out callously, 'The chances are that your business will never get off the ground and I'll end up cheated of the money you owe me.'

'It won't fail!' It was a pledge, a promise, a prayer. 'I'll work so hard, I'll make it succeed! I'll pay you back! You won't lose out!'

'How can you be sure?'

'I'm sure! I can do it!'

'You have no guarantee.'

'You don't know what I'm capable of!'

'Precisely. That's why I can't take such a risk.' He held up his hand, silencing further protest. 'That's why I would prefer to stick to my own proposition.'

Lisa sank back against the sofa, despair rushing through her. She was lost. He had rejected the best deal she could offer him. All her dreams, in an instant, had vaporised into nothing—for she knew she would never accept his proposition.

She said, 'You're wasting your time, Mr Vass. I'm not in the market for your sort of proposition.'

Black eyebrows lifted. His eyes scanned her slim figure, slumped now dispiritedly against the sofa cushions. 'You're wrong. If I may say so, you're very much in the market. My proposition, I assure you, would be to our mutual benefit.'

What a businesslike way of putting it! Lisa scythed him a look of anger. 'What a pity, in that case,' she put to him with sarcasm, 'that I find the idea so utterly repugnant!'

'Repugnant?' He delivered her a long look, then smiled. 'That's not a word I've ever heard used before in this connection. Stimulating. . .exciting. . .rewarding. . .addictive. . .' He held her eyes with a bold look, bringing a faint blush to her cheeks. And for a moment Lisa was suddenly so overcome by the confusion of responses that went rushing through her that she almost failed to pick up what he said next. 'These are more the sorts of descriptions that people tend to use about the experience of working for me.'

Lisa's jaw dropped open. 'Working? Did you say "working"?'

'Of course I said "working". What else did you expect?'

He knew what she had expected. He had deliberately led her on. Lisa glowered across at him. 'I didn't expect anything.'

Her annoyance simply amused him. 'Don't worry, my dear Lisa. The area of my life for which you believed yourself a candidate is being taken care of quite adequately at the moment. However, in the future, should I have a vacancy for the role of mistress, I shall most certainly keep you informed.'

Lisa had not expected that of him. His frankness took her by surprise. There are many hidden sides to this man, she decided, fighting to keep the colour from rising to her cheeks again. And every single one of those sides is deplorable!

Her eyes tore into him. 'Save yourself the trouble. That area of your life not only is of no interest to me, but I also consider it in very poor taste that you should have brought it up in the first place!'

That sounded a trifle prudish, which wasn't like her, but this man most definitely needed putting in his place!

Alas, however, that was not the way to do it. Alexander Vass simply looked straight through her with those penetrating coal-black eyes of his. 'Forgive me,' he enjoined her, his tone edged with mockery, 'but it was you, was it not, who introduced the subject?'

As she was about to protest he continued smoothly, 'Not directly, I'll grant you that. Not in so many words. But it seemed to me you'd made certain assumptions. . .' His gaze flickered an instant, making her blood rush. 'I thought it prudent to put you right.'

Lisa despised herself for that treacherous reaction. She'd felt a warmth go through her, as though he'd reached out and touched her, an imaginary touch that had filled her with excitement.

She threw the feeling from her and told him angrily, 'I think you wanted me to make these assumptions, Mr Vass. I think you were amusing yourself at my expense.'

His eyes widened at her bluntness and that made her feel better. Probably he was unused to such directness from lowly individuals such as herself—individuals incapable of producing at short notice trifling sums like three and a half thousand pounds!

Well, that was fine! Let him realise one thing: she might be poor, but she was nobody's doormat!

He said, 'That was most improper of me if I did. But I think, my dear Lisa, if you cast your mind back you'll recall that you made the assumption all by yourself. If anyone should be angry it is I. That was a most insulting assumption to make about any gentleman.'

As their eyes met and held, the message in his was as unreadable to Lisa as though it were written in Sanskrit. Was he joking? Was he serious? Was he making fun of her? There was absolutely no way of telling. And it struck her again, even more forcefully than before, that Alexander Vass was a hard man to fathom.

Her eyes narrowed momentarily. He was a water sign, she could sense it. He had that elusive quality so distinctive of Cancer, Scorpio and Pisces. But which one of the three star signs did he belong to? she wondered.

Whatever. . .As an Arien, her own way was more straightforward. She put to him, not without an edge of irony, 'If I offended you I apologise. That was not my intention.' She paused. 'And now, if we could get back to the point, I believe you were about to explain to me about this proposition of yours?'

'Indeed I was.' Vass leaned forward in his seat, reached for his coffee-cup and quickly drained it. He motioned towards Lisa's cup. 'Would you like more coffee?'

As he glanced up at her Lisa guessed what lay behind the gesture. Alexander Vass was subtly demonstrating that he chose his own time and his own way of doing things. He was not about to be railroaded by some impatient young woman.

She decided to play it his way. At least for the moment. 'No, thank you. I'm fine.' With an effort, she kept smiling as he topped up his own cup, added sugar, stirred, and unhurriedly raised the cup to his lips.

Then he laid it down again and sat back in his seat, resting his dark head lightly against the cushions. 'This proposition of mine. . .I'll put it to you simply. . .Come to work for me and I'll forget about the money you owe me.'

So, it was out at last, and it was not what she'd expected. She put into words the first question of many that instantly sprang into her head. 'Why on earth would you want me to come and work for you?'

'You're a designer, aren't you?'

'Yes, but not your sort of designer. As I seem to remember telling you yesterday, I design for a totally different market from G.W. Fashions.'

'Yes, you did tell me that. Old-fashioned and fuddy-duddy—these are the words, are they not, that you used to describe my company?'

Lisa had not forgotten and she did not try to deny it. 'Yes,' she agreed. 'And, I think, with some justification.'

There was a momentary silence as she waited for his

answer. She tried to read his eyes. Had she offended him?

But his next words surprised her. 'I'm in total agreement. G.W. Fashions' current lines are far from stylish. That's why I need some new blood in the design department. Someone with new ideas who can update our collections.'

'But you can't mean me! It wouldn't work!' What he was proposing, quite simply, appalled her. 'The sorts of designs that I'm planning to start work on wouldn't just update your collections, Mr Vass, they would cause a total revolution!'

'That sounds a little extreme. Not exactly what I was aiming for. What I had in mind was more along the lines of evolution than revolution.'

'So, you see, I'm really not your girl.' She sprang upon the distinction with a sense of relief. He had talked himself out of his proposition already!

But she was wrong about that. He'd talked himself out of nothing. On the contrary, he informed her, 'I've run a few checks on you, and I like what I've heard. You're hard-working and you have talent.

'Of course,' he continued, 'you may have to restrain yourself. As I said, a revolution is not what I'm after. What we need at G.W. is a designer who can appeal to a new market of younger customers without losing the loyalty of our more traditional clientele—who are far from all being,' he added with a twist of humour, 'retired country ladies, as I recall you suggested.'

His humorous reminder floated over her. He was boxing her in and Lisa was starting to panic. 'But I'm not prepared to restrain myself!' she protested in desperation. I've been restraining myself for six and a half years! That's why I'm determined to set up business for myself. So I don't have to restrain myself any more! So I can produce the sorts of designs I've always wanted to produce!'

It seemed he'd only half heard her. 'What's the problem? Are you afraid of the challenge of working for G.W. Fashions?'

'Of course I'm not! I love a challenge!' That was true. It was part of her spirited nature. 'I simply prefer the challenge of working for myself!'

'Why? So you can see your own name on your garments? You'll have that with me. I guarantee it. All your designs will bear the label "Lisa Howell for G.W. Fashions".'

'But that's not the same as running my own business!' The more she argued, the more she felt she was treading quicksand. If ever she'd seen determination shining from a man's face she could see it shining from Alexander Vass's now. 'Besides,' she added lamely, 'you haven't got any vacancies.'

'Don't worry, I shall create all the vacancies I need.'

As he smiled Lisa sensed he believed he'd won her over. Quickly, she put him right. 'It wouldn't work, Mr Vass. I promise you it wouldn't. You wouldn't be happy with me working in your design studio and I wouldn't be happy working for you.'

'In that case, perhaps you'd better just pay off your debt to me and find yourself a job as a salesgirl in some shop. No doubt you'd be happier doing that?'

The cool threat chilled her to the bone. She swallowed and almost pleaded, 'You wouldn't seriously take that money away from me?' Her voice trembled as she said it. In her heart she knew he would.

Without a word Alexander Vass rose to his feet and crossed to a small desk at the far side of the room. With his back to her he opened the leather briefcase that lay there, withdrew a buff folder and refastened the briefcase.

Lisa watched in silence, absorbing the calm movements and the total lack of caring she could sense in him. He would destroy her dreams and think nothing of it. He would use her as one used a paper towel, as an object of little worth that one just happened to find useful. Then when he'd done with her he'd screw her up and throw her away.

She felt a surge of helpless anguish, but more sharply she felt anger. She would not just sit there and let him do this to her!

As he turned once more to face her, the file in one hand, Lisa sprang to her feet and stepped towards him. 'I can't allow you to do this. I can't let you push me into a corner!'

He stopped a couple of feet away. He seemed to tower over her. 'You're not being pushed into a corner,' he told her calmly. 'What's happening is that you're being offered a way out.'

'That's not the way I see it. You're leaving me no alternative. You're forcing me. You're making threats.'

'All I'm forcing you to do is face reality. And I'm not threatening you; what I'm doing is making you an offer. I need a new designer and you need to find a way out of a considerable financial mess. Agree to work for me and we'll both have solved our problems.'

'I don't want to work for you! In fact, I refuse!' Belligerently she folded her arms across her chest.

'That's your privilege.' He continued to stand before her, his arms by his sides, his expression unruffled. 'I presume you have an alternative solution to offer?'

'Yes, I do.' Lisa's whole body was trembling. She hated Alexander Vass. If she'd had the power at that moment she would have reached out and crushed him into the carpet.

She said, keeping her anger under tight control—he would not, she sensed, be moved by ranting and raving— 'We'll come to some arrangement. I'll pay you back in instalments. With interest, as I've already suggested. And you,' she added, not quite politely, 'can go and look somewhere else for your new designer.'

Alexander Vass said nothing for a moment. Those mysterious dark eyes of his drifted over her, unhurriedly, seeming to burn where they touched her.

Then he surprised her by asking, 'Just one thing bothers me. Why were you never promoted in your previous company? How come you never rose above the level of staff designer?'

'I wasn't good enough!' Lisa seized her opportunity. 'Take my word for it, I'd be no good to you at G.W. Fashions!'

She pressed her lips together so she wouldn't spout the truth. The last thing she wanted, now that she had gained a small advantage, was to blow that advantage by telling him the truth.

For the truth was that she'd been offered promotion a dozen times—in spite of the fact that when she'd started as a trainee she'd had no formal training, no experience, nothing to commend her but a fistful of ambition. But over the years she'd studied hard— correspondence courses, night classes, anything she could lay her hands on. In the end she'd been too good for her lowly position.

She'd turned down the offers of promotion because of Emily. Promotion would have meant more hours at the workroom, plus a not inconsiderable amount of travelling around the country, and she had decided that she would wait until her daughter went to school before considering such a career move. It had been a difficult decision, but she was sure it had been the right one.

Vass looked at her hard. 'I confess that that surprises me. I confess that in spite of the many negative sides I can see to you I would have expected you to be good management material.' He paused. 'Perhaps, after all, I misjudged you.'

'I fear you did.' Lisa's inward smile grew wider. The real reason for her lack of promotion, she knew, would never in a million years occur to him. Men didn't think about such things.

He sighed and shrugged. 'Ah, well. . .' he murmured.

Lisa tensed. Was he about to withdraw his proposal? With every atom of her being she was praying that he was.

Then he shrugged again, raising her hopes even higher, and the black eyes looked at her long and hard. 'In that case. . .' he began.

Lisa crossed her fingers.

'. . .in that case,' he continued, 'I suppose it would

be unwise. . .' He paused again, driving her crazy. Then he smiled. 'It would be unwise, I suppose, to have too high hopes of you. . .but I'm prepared to take a chance.

'You'll regret it! I won't work for you! Don't try to make me!' Semi-coherent with frustration, Lisa protested. 'Don't force me! I'll make you sorry if you do!'

The dark eyebrows lifted. 'Is that a threat, my dear Lisa? And how do you plan to make me sorry? Tell me that.'

Lisa had no answer. The words had tumbled out in anger. She scarcely knew any more what she was saying.

Impetuously she stepped towards him, closing the gap between them. 'Please, Mr Vass. Don't do this to me. I may never have another chance to set up my own business. . .and it means so much to me. . .You have no idea.'

'Perhaps I do.' The dark eyes seemed to soften. Unexpectedly he reached out and lightly touched her cheek. 'But I'm doing you a favour. Going it alone is a dangerous business. What I'm offering you is something much less risky. A steady job with a damned good salary. . .'

His fingers were like fire as they scorched across her skin, and suddenly, as a charge of electricity shot through her, Lisa felt riveted to the spot. Invisible nails held her feet to the floor. All her strength had left her. She could not move a step.

She looked up into those eyes, suddenly as deep and soft as velvet, aware that his words were spinning shapelessly in her head.

Risky. . .dangerous. . .Her mind bent and twisted. The words on his lips were the words that described him. Yet, though she longed to flee from him, to put huge distances between them, there was something drawing her, some mystery in him that seemed to reach out and take her in its clutches. The strength of its hold on her gave her goose-bumps.

He was saying, 'Why take an unnecessary risk? What I'm offering you is the ideal solution.'

His fingers curved beneath her chin, his touch firm yet gentle. Her body was melting. She wanted to give in.

But then his fingers grew harder. 'Besides,' he added softly, 'if you think about it sensibly, you really have no alternative.'

His words were like a sharp slap that brought her to her senses. Lisa stepped back away from him, shaken and appalled at herself. Just for a moment back there he had hypnotised her. Literally.

She glared into his face. 'No!' she spat defiantly. 'Never! I'll never do what you say!'

He was unmoved by her outburst. He held up the buff folder. 'In here are some facts and figures that I'm sure will interest you. They concern the design section of G.W. Fashions—the department you'll be joining shortly as head.' He nodded in the direction of the sofa. 'I suggest we sit down while I explain them to you briefly.'

Lisa was back in control again, the spell was broken, but still she knew that she was beaten. She looked up into his face and resisted the urge to snatch the folder from his hand and strew its contents defiantly across the carpet. How she would have loved to have permitted herself that gesture, then to have stalked out of the room and slammed the door.

Instead, feeling as though with each step she took she was treading on her dreams, destroying them forever, she followed him mutely back to the sofa and seated herself where she had been before.

But she would make him pay for this, she vowed to herself silently, even if she killed herself in the process!

CHAPTER FOUR

LISA drove home just over an hour later in a state of such fury that she could barely focus. She had lost the battle. Vass was the victor. Her tears held in check, she'd kissed goodbye to her future.

Back at the hotel, after finally conceding that there was no way out of her financial dilemma other than to go to work for G.W. Fashions, Lisa had demanded, as Vass had sat there drinking coffee, oblivious of the callous blow he had inflicted, 'So, how long is this arrangement supposed to last? How long do you propose keeping me chained to my desk?'

He had smiled at that. 'I doubt that chains will be necessary. My workforce has a reputation for being committed to the company. I'm sure you'll soon find that that applies to you, too.'

Lisa, seated stiffly on the sofa opposite him, had pulled a defiantly sceptical face. 'I wouldn't count on it. You can hardly expect commitment and company loyalty from an employee who's been press-ganged into working for you. Surely that would be just a little unrealistic?'

Vass blithely ignored her charge that she'd been press-ganged. That was a *fait accompli*, no longer worth discussing.

He said instead, 'You'll enjoy working for me. You said you're a girl who enjoys a challenge. You'll find

55

no shortage of challenges at G.W. Fashions. And your first challenge will be to design a new spring-summer collection, to be ready at the latest by the end of December.'

'But that's less than three months away! I can't possibly do it!'

'Of course you can do it. You'll have plenty of assistance. As I said, regard it as a challenge.'

He was manipulating her shamelessly and it was intensely irritating that he had homed in so accurately on the most effective way of doing it—not by bullying, but by appealing to her competitive instincts.

Lisa threw him a diminishing look. She knew what he was up to. 'Perhaps I prefer to pick my own challenges,' she informed him sharply. 'Perhaps I don't respond to challenges that are imposed on me by others!'

Vass responded with a long look. His eyes seemed to search deep into her. 'It is a lucky man or woman,' he told her in a soft voice, 'who is blessed with the privilege of being able to pick and choose the challenges he or she must face in life. The biggest challenges that most of us have to deal with are invariably those that are thrown at us by fate.'

There was something about the way he said it, in a tone of calm wisdom, that just for a moment made Lisa curious. Who was Alexander Vass? She knew nothing about him beyond the fact that he was immensely wealthy, the owner of the London-based Silver Star Navigation who for some strange reason had branched out into the fashion industry.

It was gone in a moment, but briefly she'd been filled

with a sudden, oddly urgent desire to know more about him.

He added, 'It is these unexpected challenges, and how we respond to them, that build our characters and make us what we are.'

Lisa might have responded that over the past few years she'd endured more than her share of character-building challenges. But that, she sensed, would sound self-pitying and, in turn, would only invite his scorn. He was not a man, she had decided, much given to compassion.

Instead she responded, 'I wonder what made *you* what you are? I wonder what makes a man so unforgiving and hard?'

It had been intended, purely and simply, as an insult, but it had come out with just a hint of that genuine curiosity that so unexpectedly had afflicted her just a moment before.

His sharp ears, predictably, had picked up that nuance. The black eyes glinted. 'Perhaps, one day, I'll tell you. One day when we've got to know each other a little better.'

His words caused an unexpected shiver to go through her, part excitement, part fear. She felt a swift flash of danger. Her back seemed to press a little harder against the cushions.

She took a deep breath. 'That won't be necessary. I'm not really interested. It was just an idle observation.' Having made that clear, she felt instantly less threatened. She narrowed her eyes at him over the coffee-table. 'But there is one thing that does very much interest me, as it happens. . .and that's your answer to my question. . .the one I asked five minutes ago and to which you have so far avoided giving an answer. . .' She tilted her chin at him. 'How long do you intend forcing me to work for you?'

Vass leaned back in his seat, resting his dark head against the silk cushions. His eyes flicked over her. 'In order to answer that, I need you to answer me one question. . .'

'What question?' Lisa countered, her stomach tightening.

'One very simple question. Namely this. . .' he paused, regarding her through long, thick lashes '. . .if I had agreed to your proposal to pay off your debt to me in instalments, how long do you reckon it would have taken you?'

'To pay it all back? To write the debt off completely?'

'Precisely.' He nodded. 'To pay back every penny.'

'That's not easy to calculate. I can't be certain how much I would have been earning working for myself. . .'

'Two years? Three years? Five years? Ten? Surely you must have some idea?'

'Well, certainly not ten. That would be a little pessimistic. I think two to three years would be a pretty fair estimate.'

'Two to three years?' He seemed to ponder. Then he nodded. 'That sounds fair.' He stretched his long legs out in front of him and seemed to examine his shiny black shoes for a moment. 'In that case, I would say it was reasonable. . .' as he spoke his eyes drifted up to meet hers again '. . .I would say it was reasonable, since under our current agreement I shall be totally cancelling out your debt, that you contract to remain in my employ for three years.'

Lisa gasped for breath. Her heart had stopped within her. 'Three years?' she exclaimed, horrified. 'Surely you can't be serious?'

'You think that excessive?' His expression had not altered. There was neither surprise nor concern on his face at her reaction. 'You said yourself it would have taken you around three years to pay me back.'

'But that's not the same!'

'Isn't it? Why not? All I'm doing is trading your debt for your time.'

'But it's not the same! It's utterly ridiculous. I said two to three years, I don't deny it, but I wouldn't have been spending every minute of that time working to pay off what I owed you. I'd have been making a living for myself as well!'

'And you'll be making a living while you're working for me—or do you intend to take no salary?'

Lisa frowned at him. 'Of course I don't. How could I possibly live without a salary?'

'That's what I thought.' He held her eyes. 'And, if I may say so, my suspicions are that you'll be making a considerably better living on the salary I pay you than you would have made working for yourself. . .'

'Regrettably, that's something that neither of us will ever know.' She bit the accusation at him resentfully. 'For all either of us knows my business might have boomed. I might have been able to pay you off within six months!' Suddenly she was regretting her earlier estimate. Look at where her caution had landed her!

'So, you believe in miracles?' Alexander Vass was smiling, that smile she had seen before that totally transformed him. 'I thought the age of miracles was supposed to be past?'

'Not if you believe in them.' Lisa was vehement. 'If you believe in miracles you can make them happen!'

For one revealing instant her heart was in her eyes. She did believe that. She had proved it to herself. Hadn't she known, six years ago, pregnant and alone, that it would take a miracle for her to survive Tony's death and build some kind of life for herself and her child? And the miracle had happened. She had made it happen. And she could have done it again if only she'd had the chance.

Her eyes burned into Vass's as his smile abruptly faded. He did not believe her. He thought her foolish. But then a man like him was in no need of miracles.

He observed in a mocking tone, 'I think six months would be pushing it, even if you managed to summon up a miracle. Your original estimate, I think, was more realistic. Though even to have achieved that, may I presume to suggest, might have required a certain degree of divine intervention.'

Lisa looked back hard at him. 'Say what you like, there's no way I'm going to agree to work for you for three years. I'd sooner wind up in a debtors' prison!'

Again that flash of a smile illuminated his features. He had this quirky sense of humour that always seemed to surface whenever Lisa least expected it.

He leaned towards her. 'OK,' he conceded, taking her yet again by surprise. 'Three years, I admit, is rather a long time. I doubt that either of us could survive such a lengthy association.' He paused. 'I'll reduce it by fifty per cent. Instead of three years, we'll make it eighteen months. Eighteen months, starting from tomorrow.'

That was better, but it was still an unendurable chasm of time. Lisa bent towards him. 'A year,' she countered. 'Make it a year and I'll agree.'

'Sorry. Eighteen months is my final offer.' Vass rose to his feet. 'Take it or leave it.'

'A year,' Lisa insisted, feeling the water close over her. 'Make it a year. A year is more than long enough.'

He ignored her entreaties. 'Those papers on the coffee-table.' He nodded to the pile of papers he'd withdrawn earlier from his briefcase. 'They'll tell you all you need to know about the design department at G.W., so kindly make sure you've read and understood them before you report for work tomorrow morning.'

There was no point in insisting. It would do her no good now. From the tone of his voice, it was perfectly clear that his decision was not open to negotiation. He might even increase her sentence if she continued to argue.

Lisa glanced defeatedly at the pile of papers, then with a heavy heart she gathered them up. She glanced defiantly at Vass as she rose to her feet.

'You may think you've won, but I'll have the last laugh. I'll make you sorry you ever met me!'

He had risen ahead of her and was standing by the door now, pulling it open, inviting her to leave. He pierced her with a look. 'Don't make threats,' he warned her. 'I don't like threats. I don't like them in the slightest.'

These had been the last words that had passed
between them. Lisa had flung out through the door
without so much as a glance at him, and on legs made
of rubber had fled to the lift. Then she had made her
way swiftly across the hotel lobby and out into the car
park where she'd left her little Mini.

Now, as she drove home, still livid with anger, she
was aware of a growing sense of desolation. As long as
she'd been fighting him there had still been a hope that
she might eventually emerge the victor. That hope had
now been shattered. The battle was over and the future
she had dreamed of lay all about her in hopeless ruins.

Lisa smiled bitterly to herself. If only it were possible
to carry out that silly threat she'd made—to make him
sorry he'd ever met her. But the truth was it had meant
nothing, nothing at all. All it had been was a futile
expression of the frustration and anger that bubbled
inside her.

She banged her fist against the steering-wheel, fighting back the tears that scalded her eyes and threatened
to blind her. All because of one silly accident, which
hadn't even been her fault, her life for the next long
miserable eighteen months was to be ruled by a man
whom she detested with all her heart.

That night Lisa lay sleepless, staring into the darkness.
She should look on the bright side, she kept trying to
tell herself. At least she wasn't being forced to fork out
the three and a half thousand pounds. At least she
wasn't being left penniless and in debt, with nothing.
She could cancel the bank loan and salt away her

redundancy money and pick up her plans to start her own business as soon as the eighteen months were up.

But it seemed so far away. Eighteen months was like a lifetime. And eighteen months working for Alexander Vass would be more like a dozen miserable lifetimes!

She punched her pillow. She felt like a prisoner. In chains and at the mercy of that detestable man!

Then she gritted her teeth. She would not let him defeat her. She would not allow herself to feel like his prisoner.

She *would* be positive. She *would* look on the bright side. Optimism, after all, was a part of her Arien nature. She would treat this as an unexpected opportunity to gain experience in mass-production fashion. If it killed her, she would turn the situation around and gain from it something instructive and valuable!

She would make the disaster serve her rather than drag her under. She would not let it beat her. She would turn it to her advantage!

And besides, it occurred to her, there was one huge consolation that she had not so far fully considered. . .

Though she was being forced to work for Vass, at least she could be thankful that she would not be called upon to endure the misery of working *alongside* him! Silver Star Navigation, the centre of his empire, was based in London, and consequently it was in London that her future boss spent most of his time. As she dwelt upon that thought Lisa began to feel better.

She relaxed and closed her eyes, the tension leaving her. And less than two minutes later she was sleeping as peacefully as the five-year-old child in the bedroom next door.

'Naturally, I demand your written undertaking that the eighteen months' hard labour I have agreed to do here cancels out, fully and forever, the three and a half thousand pounds I owe you.'

It was seven minutes past nine the following morning and Lisa was standing in Alexander Vass's office, having reported for duty fifteen minutes earlier.

She'd arrived early, intending, if she could, to wrong-foot him. He'd be expecting her to come dragging in at least ten minutes late, with a scowl on her face, unwilling and reluctant. He'd be thrown when she turned up, looking keen and eager, demanding to be shown instantly to her desk.

Her plan had misfired. He had not appeared thrown, and neither in the slightest had he been wrong-footed. He had glanced up at her as she'd swept into his office, dressed in a pair of slim navy trousers and a plain navy top, her working gear, and told her, 'Take a seat. I'll be with you in a moment.'

It was as though he'd known she'd appear at precisely that moment with precisely that eager expression on her face.

Lisa had had this feeling before, that he could predict her behaviour, that he could see just a little too clearly inside her head. And it annoyed her intensely, not least of all because she still felt a long way from figuring *him* out!

That was why, perversely, she'd remained standing where she was, pointedly disdaining his invitation to sit down—though it occurred to her, increasing her sense of irritation, that, quite possibly, that was precisely the reaction he'd anticipated!

She was still standing there now, waiting impatiently, as he glanced through some papers, scribbling notes here and there. Though she was wishing that, after all, she'd taken a seat, for she suspected he was rather enjoying letting her stew in her own juice.

Indeed, when at last he tossed aside his pen, sat back in his chair and raised his eyes to hers, there was a hint of amusement deep in the dark eyes. What side of him was she about to have inflicted on her now?

And in that instant she guessed the stars that ruled him. He was a Cancer, ever-changing, unpredictable, as bright and as mysterious as the moon.

'So, you wish to formalise our arrangement with a written contract?' The amusement in his eyes was tautly echoed in his voice. 'Should I take that to mean that you do not trust me?'

Lisa was tempted to respond, yes, that was precisely how he ought to take it, but decided that might be unnecessarily forthright. And not quite in keeping with the positive approach she was committed to.

With a diplomatic smile, she expressed herself more subtly. 'I'm a believer in getting things down in black and white. That way everyone knows exactly where they stand.'

'But we already know where we stand, do we not?' Alexander Vass raised one jet-black eyebrow. 'Why do we have need of bits of paper?'

'Just in case.'

'Just in case what?'

'Just in case at some future date we find ourselves needing to refer back to our agreement.' He was being deliberately perverse, but she would not give in to him. 'If we have a written record, an agreement, signed by both of us, there can be no misinterpretation of what was intended.'

'Misinterpretation?' He seemed to consider the term a moment. 'I think I was right. You do not trust me.'

Lisa looked into his face. He was enjoying this hugely. 'You might forget,' she pointed out. 'Things slip our minds with time. You might not remember exactly what we agreed to.'

Vass shook his head. 'Lay your fears to rest. I assure you, my dear Lisa, I have an excellent memory.' Then as she stepped towards his desk, a further protest on her lips, he put to her flatly, looking her in the eye, 'Are you afraid that, once the eighteen months are over, I might change my mind and refuse to release you? Is that the worry that's bothering you so much?'

That was precisely the worry that was bothering her so much.

Lisa met his gaze frankly. 'As a matter of fact, yes.'

Alexander Vass smiled. 'Then don't worry any longer. I promise you I have every intention of releasing you the moment the eighteen months are up.'

'That's not good enough!'

'I'm afraid it will have to be.' The amusement had left his voice. The words had been spoken with the finality of a full stop. He leaned back in his chair and surveyed her for a moment. 'Besides, has the possibility not occurred to you that you yourself may not wish to be released? When the time comes for me to show you to the door you may be down on your knees, begging to be kept on.'

That was possibly the most humorous thing she had ever heard. Lisa laughed. 'And fish might grow beards!' she taunted. 'Don't worry, Mr Vass, there's not the slightest chance of my wishing to prolong the agony of our arrangement. I'll be off like a shot the moment my time's up.'

'We'll see. You might surprise yourself.' He smiled an enigmatic smile. 'And, by the way, as I've already told you once before, I'd prefer you to call me Alexander. Your rank as senior designer warrants a certain waiving of the formalities.'

Lisa looked back at him. She possessed a vivid imagination, but somehow, no matter how hard she tried, she could not envisage herself ever calling this man Alexander. To do so would imply a certain easiness between them. Sympathy, even. And that would never happen.

She said, her tone deliberately confrontational, pointedly passing no comment on his invitation, 'Aren't you a little worried about leaving me here in charge? I might get up to all sorts of little tricks.'

'What sort of little tricks?' One eyebrow lifted.

'I might direct your design team to produce completely the wrong designs for you. You've put me in a position where it would be very easy for me to sabotage your plans.'

The other eyebrow lifted to form a bridge with its neighbour. 'I don't like that word "sabotage". Don't ever use it again. Not even jokingly,' he reprimanded sharply.

Then the dark eyebrows lowered. 'But, to answer
your question, no, I'm not worried that you'll take
advantage of your position to misdirect my designers.
Not out of any love or loyalty for me, but because it
would not be in your interests to do so. . .'

'If I could put you out of business it would be very
much in my interests. It would mean I'd be free of you
that much sooner!'

'Perhaps. But that is not your prime consideration.'
He leaned back in his chair. 'You see, Lisa, I've
understood you. I know what makes you tick.' As she
scowled he continued, 'You'll make the best of this
opportunity. As I've told you, your designs will carry
your name. And that matters to you. That's why I
know you'll do your best.'

Lisa felt her scowl deepen. It was starting to be
unnerving, this ability of his to judge her with such
uncanny accuracy!

His eyes held hers. 'I'm right, am I not? I can rely
on you?'

Lisa glanced away, then let her gaze slide back to
him. 'I guess that's something you'll just have to wait
and see.' Her eyes sparked a challenge. 'You'll just
have to trust me.'

'Trust you. . .yes. But I'll also be keeping an eye on
you.'

'From London?' Her tone was scoffing. 'That won't
be easy!'

'No, it wouldn't be, would it? But I won't be in
London.' He paused a beat, causing her to tense in
anticipation. 'Where I'll be is right here in Liskeard,
for the most part seated at this very desk.' He smiled

in the face of her sudden pallor. 'I think you will agree that that will make it extremely easy for me to keep a constant eye on you?'

'But what about your company, Silver Star Navigation? That's your main business. Shouldn't you be looking after that?'

The note of mild panic in her voice did not elude him. Alexander Vass smiled without compassion across at her. 'Your concern is most touching, but quite unnecessary. Arrangements have been made. You may set your mind at rest.'

'But——'

'So, you see, we'll be working closely together.' He rose to his feet. 'Personally, I'm rather looking forward to it.'

Lisa stared back at him in sudden speechless misery. Perhaps she'd made the wrong choice, after all, she was thinking. Perhaps destitution might have been preferable to this.

But it was too late now for recriminations. He was sweeping round the desk, coming to stand before her. 'Come. I'll introduce you to the rest of the staff. Then you can get down to some work and start paying off your debt.'

He smiled as he said it, but Lisa did not smile back. For one thing, she did not find the prospect amusing, and for another, all at once she found herself stricken, her muscles as though atrophied by his nearness.

She took a shaky step back, mentally berating herself for continuing to react to him in this inexplicable fashion. Inexplicable and downright humiliating, she thought angrily. His physical proximity invariably seemed to provoke in her sensations with which she was quite unfamiliar. She felt breathless, light-headed and as perfectly helpless as a butterfly whose wings had been pinned behind its back.

But already he was sweeping past her, heading for the door, quite unaware of her inner anguish. As she followed him, snatching her wits together again, she asked, 'When did your senior designer resign? As I told you, when my friend enquired about a job a couple of weeks ago she was told there were no vacancies at all.'

'No, there wouldn't have been.' He held the door open, inviting her to step into the corridor.

'So he or she resigned rather suddenly?'

'He or she did not resign at all.' He held her gaze as she stepped briskly past him. 'I fired him yesterday, as a matter of fact.'

'Fired him? Why?' She felt a dart of worry.

And, instantly, he confirmed her premonition. 'To make room for you. Why else, my dear Lisa? I could scarcely employ two senior designers.'

Lisa stepped out into the corridor with a sinking feeling. That was just terrific, she was thinking. She was about to take on a job whose previous holder had just been fired specifically to make room for her. She could just imagine the welcome she was about to get from her workmates!

Alexander Vass appeared to have read her mind. He glanced at her over his shoulder as he led her down the corridor. 'Don't worry,' he smiled, 'I'm here to protect you. Any problems, just come straight to me.'

Then he was striding off towards the design-room, a subdued and anxious Lisa at his heels.

What had she got herself into? What had *he* got her into? Things seemed to be getting worse with every step she took.

She glared at his back. How she hated this man!

CHAPTER FIVE

IN FACT, to Lisa's relief and surprise, her reception from her new workmates was fairly friendly—though tinged with that nervous wariness that always greeted a new broom.

No one mentioned Nigel, her ousted predecessor, and for the moment Lisa decided to steer clear of that subject. Only once the others had become used to her, once she had made a few allies, would she risk stirring up so sensitive a subject.

The staff in the main were machine operators, whose jobs ranged from cutting out the designs from the cloth to skilfully stitching the garments together. On the design side, besides herself, there were two assistant designers, Leo and Kerry, both younger than herself, and both, judging by the samples of work they showed Lisa, highly competent in the tasks of pattern-making and fitting, but not quite up to producing original designs themselves.

That was all right with Lisa. At this stage it suited her to work entirely on her own. Eventually she would train them to produce the kinds of designs she favoured, but for the moment, until she had her first collection down on paper, quite frankly she couldn't spare the time.

And she wasted not a moment. Even her very first

day was spent bent over her desk, scribbling and sketching furiously.

'I see you're taking this job extremely seriously,' Leo offered sympathetically as he brought her a cup of coffee halfway through the afternoon. 'You've been working like a Trojan all day!'

'I'll be working like a Trojan for the next twelve weeks,' Lisa smiled back as she thanked him for the coffee. 'That's the only way I'm going to get a new collection ready!'

But I'll do it! she told herself, her enthusiasm for the task growing with every stroke of her charcoal pencil. And the ideas were flowing. Like a woman inspired, she was dashing off design after design, as though nothing could stop her.

Three days had passed before it suddenly struck Lisa that she had so far been spared her most dreaded aggravation—the aggravation of Alexander Vass constantly breathing down her neck.

She had passed him once or twice, fleetingly, in the corridor, when all he had subjected her to was a brief 'good morning'. And he had stopped her in the lobby once to enquire, 'How are things going? Any problems?' 'No problems,' she'd responded, expecting to be asked to elaborate. But he had simply nodded, 'Good,' and left it at that.

Of course, she knew it would be foolish of her to imagine that this benign state of affairs could possibly last. Sooner or later he would emerge from the woodwork and proceed to make a bearable situation unbearable.

She was absolutely right. And it was sooner, not later.

It was mid-afternoon the following day—a Thursday—when the phone on her desk began to ring. Lisa knew it was Vass, even before she reached to answer it. She picked up the receiver resignedly. 'Hello? Lisa here.'

'Come to my office. Immediately,' he told her. 'I want to know what you've been doing for the past four days.'

That was it. The phone went dead. Lisa was instantly aware of her muscles tightening. Adrenalin rushed through her. She could feel her breathing quicken. Quite involuntarily her body was getting ready for a fight.

Keep calm, she told herself. Don't let him ruffle you. Treat him with the utter contempt he deserves.

Two minutes later she was tapping on his office door, clutching to her bosom the file of notes and sketches that she had been working on with such enthusiasm all week.

'Come in!'

It was a command, not an invitation. As Lisa pushed the door open she felt a rush of antipathy at the sight of the dark figure seated behind the desk. And her antipathy increased as he waved magisterially and told her, 'Take a seat.'

Lisa sat, arranging herself on the edge of one of the chairs, the stiff posture of one who would prefer not to linger. She never felt particularly at ease in his office. It felt too functional—and unwelcoming, just like its owner.

'So, what have you been up to?' Vass leaned back in his chair and subjected her to one of those arrogant black looks of his. He was not, Lisa thought wryly, feeling jovial today.

'I've been busy,' she told him. 'Exceedingly busy.'

'So it would seem. Every time I've passed the studio you've been sitting with your head bent, scribbling away. Perhaps you'd care to enlighten me as to what exactly you've been doing?'

So, he'd been spying on her, had he? That annoyed her!

She said, with a brief nod at the file on her lap, 'I've been doing what you asked me to do. I've been designing a new collection.'

Vass reached across the desk to take the file of designs from her. 'I'm impressed,' he observed, holding her gaze for a moment. 'I hadn't expected you to make so much progress so quickly.'

'Hadn't you? Then I'm happy to be able to surprise you. I've made a great deal of progress, as you can see.'

'Indeed it would seem so. And, as I say, I'm astonished. I had expected you to spend your first week just finding your feet.' As he spoke he flicked through the file of drawings, his expression giving absolutely nothing away. 'I had expected it would take a little while just to organise your thoughts.'

Lisa smiled smugly. 'That wasn't necessary. My thoughts were already perfectly organised, just waiting to be put down on paper.'

'Indeed,' he said again, continuing to examine the drawings. Then he laid the file down and sat back, his eyes on her. Suddenly he said, 'How's your little girl?'

'Emily?' Lisa blinked, surprised by the question. 'Emily's fine. Why do you ask?'

He ignored that last question. 'I'm glad to hear it.' Then, arching one dark eyebrow, he enquired, 'I expect you've heard that we're opening a crèche?'

'Yes, I'd heard that.' The news had surprised her. The initiative, she had decided, must have come from someone else. Alexander Vass was not the type of man who would identify with the needs of his female staff.

'Emily's past the age for a crèche,' she told him, wondering what had prompted this digression. 'So it won't really be of any use to me.'

'Perhaps in the future. . .?'

'I hardly think so. I'm highly unlikely to find myself a husband and produce another child within the next eighteen months.'

He smiled. 'You never know.'

'But I do know,' she answered. And there was something in his smile and the way it affected her, something in the way his eyes probed into her, that prompted her to add, 'To tell the truth, I don't really expect that ever to happen.'

'Why ever not? Are you averse to marriage?'

'Not in the slightest. I loved being married.'

'Then why are you so reluctant to repeat the experience?'

He had misconstrued. She was not reluctant. But for some reason, perversely, she did not correct him. Instead, almost aggressively, she answered, 'My marriage was an experience that could never be repeated.'

'I see.' The dark eyes narrowed. He nodded slowly and she felt his gaze drift to the gold band on her wedding finger. A look crossed his eyes. She sensed he was about to say something. But then he seemed to think better of it. He observed instead, his tone reflective, almost as though he were speaking to himself, 'You manage well on your own. That's most commendable. I have a relative, a cousin, in a situation much like yours. I'm afraid she's never learned to stand on her own feet. She's always running to other members of the family—usually me—whenever she needs help.'

His praise of her was damned by that last false innuendo. Did he seriously expect her to believe, Lisa wondered, that he was some kind of defender of family life?

'You surprise me.' Lisa's tone was cutting. 'I didn't think you were a man for whom family relationships would be important.'

One eyebrow lifted. 'Why, may I ask?'

She answered in a word. 'Nigel,' she told him. Then she went on to elaborate with the facts she'd learned from Leo. 'Nigel's a married man, with a wife and two children. Yet you threw him out of his job just to make room for me.'

'Does that make you feel bad?'

'As a matter of fact, it does.'

'Then why don't you quit, if your conscience is bothering you? If you're feeling so squeamish about it, why are you still here?'

'I've thought about quitting, but you know my situation. I've a family to think of, too. Would you re-employ him if I did?'

Vass shook his head. 'No,' he told her flatly. He smiled a hard smile. 'Does that make you feel any better?'

Lisa did not answer. She looked back at him disapprovingly. He was so cruel at times, so utterly ruthless. And this dark side of his Cancerian temperament was something she found increasingly scary.

'Ah, by the way. . .' As she watched him in silence he slid open one of his desk drawers and lifted out a sheaf of papers. 'These require your signature.' He tossed the papers across the desk towards her. 'When you've finished, kindly return one copy to me.'

Lisa glanced at the papers. 'May I ask what they are?'

'They're copies of our agreement. Read the terms carefully. Then, when you're satisfied, sign both copies and keep one for yourself.'

Surprise lit up her eyes. She had abandoned all hope of getting her contract down in black and white!

Vass smiled. 'I realised you were right. This will save any wrangles later.'

'I'm glad you saw sense.' She threw him a cool look as she scooped the papers from his desk. 'I'll get one signed copy back to you immediately,' she assured him.

He was leaning back in his seat, dark eyes watching her. 'Be sure to read the contents first.'

Lisa felt herself falter at the dark note in his voice. She narrowed her eyes at him suspiciously. 'Surely I already know what the contents of our contract are— namely, that I am to work for you for a period of eighteen months, after which time you will release me with my debt to you cancelled?'

'That's basically it.'

'Basically? Why just basically? Have you added something else?'

'I've added a rider.'

'What kind of a rider?'

'A rider that I felt was necessary to protect my interests.' Vass cast a quick glance down at the file of drawings, then raised his eyes to hers again, their expression brittle. 'Now that I've seen these, I'm very glad I did.'

Lisa felt something inside her become very still. 'And what is that supposed to mean?'

His eyes lanced right through her. 'After all,' he continued, 'it's totally pointless your coming to work for me if the designs you produce don't suit my needs.'

Lisa held his gaze. 'And is that what you're saying? That you don't like these designs that I've just shown you?'

Vass sighed. 'I'm afraid they're totally unsuitable. I'm afraid they won't do at all for G.W. Fashions.'

'Why not? They're good designs!'

'Some of them are very good. But none of them is suitable for our market. I'm surprised you didn't realise that for yourself.'

'I thought you wanted something different?' Her eyes sparked at his condescension. 'Why did you go to the trouble of hiring me if what you wanted were the same drab old styles of before?'

'I don't want the same drab old styles of before, but, as I told you, neither do I want a revolution. What I want is evolution. Continuity. A continuation of the classic G.W. tradition. But updated, given a new lease of life.' He leaned back in his seat. 'Before rushing ahead with your sketches I think you might have been advised to take the time to familiarise yourself with what G.W. Fashions stands for.'

He gestured almost contemptuously at her drawings. 'And what it stands for is definitely not this.'

'In that case, I'm sorry.' Lisa was seething. 'In that case, I fail to see how we can possibly work together.'

Vass smiled a grim smile. 'It won't be easy. I'm beginning to see that all too clearly. But it can be done.' His eyes burned into hers. 'It can be done and it will be done. All you need is a little guidance.'

The words grated against her nerves. A little guidance! She glared at him. 'I thought *I* was supposed to be in charge of the design side?'

'So you are. But *I'm* in charge of G.W. Fashions. And I'm afraid that means that what I say goes.'

Damn him! Lisa glared at him. Their eyes locked together. 'I can't work like that,' she told him flatly. 'If I can't do what I want I'd rather call this whole thing off.'

'That's up to you.' Vass smiled at her coldly. 'Though I think perhaps you're forgetting the purpose of our agreement. . .I get a new designer, you pay off your debt. . .' He paused as her cheeks paled. Yes, that had slipped her mind. In the heat of her anger she had forgotten about her debt.

Vass leaned towards her, elbows propped on the desk. 'So, as I was saying. . .this agreement I've drawn up. . .In order to protect my interests, I've included a clause that states that, unless you produce suitable, usable designs, the debt, alas, will remain outstanding and will be required to be repaid in full at the end of the eighteen months.'

'But that's not fair! That's downright cheating! What's to stop you simply saying that my designs aren't suitable and demanding the money, whether it's true or not?'

'Nothing, I suppose, technically speaking.' He smiled at her callously. Then his expression sobered. 'But I think we both know that there's little likelihood of that. This venture is important to me. If you produce the right designs I'll use them. And be only too happy to give you full credit.'

He paused. 'But, if you fail, I'll show no mercy. You can absolutely bank on that.'

That scarcely needed saying. Lisa felt a chill go through her. Suddenly she was caught between a rock and a hard place.

'So, I would advise you,' he added, nodding at her folder, 'to make a bonfire with those sketches and start again from scratch.'

That did it. That final, careless insult.

Lisa glared at him. 'No, Mr Vass, I won't be making a bonfire with my sketches. They're damned good sketches, whatever you may think!' She rose to her feet. 'But, as for these. . .' with a gesture of contempt she held up the copies of the agreement '. . .there's no way in the world I'm going to sign these, so you can make a bonfire with *them*, if you like!'

So saying, with all her strength she flung them at him, so that they scythed across his desk, scattering letters and papers. Then she turned on her heel and strode stiffly from the room.

* * *

'Maybe it wasn't the wisest thing to have done,' Lisa reflected to Josey over a cup of tea that evening. 'It leaves me high and dry as far as the debt's concerned. Legally I still owe him that wretched money—whether or not I produce the sorts of designs he wants.'

Josey had popped round to spend a consoling hour with her while husband Charlie watched football on TV. She nodded in concern. 'I can understand why you're angry. He sounds like an impossible man to deal with. But if I were in your shoes I'd be worried silly with a debt of three and a half thousand hanging over me.'

She took a sip of her tea and regarded Lisa squarely. 'In your place, quite frankly, I'd sign the agreement— and then just make damned sure I produced what he wanted.'

'But Josey, what he wants is not my type of thing! He uses words like "classic" and "continuity". My whole style is innovation! Lord knows why he picked me!' Lisa sighed in frustration and sat back in her armchair, scowling down at the flickering gas fire. 'It's just no good! I just can't do it!'

Then she shook her head. 'But you're right about one thing. The thought of that debt scares me silly.'

The thought of it, in fact, kept her awake most of the night. It wasn't until dawn that she finally drifted off into an all too brief and fitful sleep.

Yet it was only as she was getting Emily ready for school next morning that she forced herself to come to a decision. She owed it to her daughter to make this compromise. It wasn't just her own future she was risking by refusing to accept Alexander Vass's terms. She was risking her daughter's future as well.

Once she had faced up to that, it was an easy decision. Lisa got to the office early and went straight to Vass's door.

'I'll sign the agreement,' she told him in clipped tones. Out of duty she had caved in, but it still went against the grain.

'So, you've decided to be co-operative? A wise decision.' He reached into his desk drawer and drew out the copies of the contract, a trifle battered by yesterday's violence, and tossed them across the desk towards her. 'I look forward to a mutually beneficial union.'

There was a smug note in his voice that grated against her nerve-ends. She picked up the two copies reluctantly, as though with tongs, and looked back across the desk at him defiantly. 'I wouldn't count your chickens, Mr Vass. I've agreed to sign the contract, but that's all I've agreed to.'

'Does that mean that you do not intend to adhere to its terms?' He smiled a warning smile. 'As I have advised you, that could prove expensive.'

Lisa had not meant that. She didn't know what she had meant, only that she felt an uncontrollable urge to thwart him.

She said, narrowing her eyes at him, 'There are ways and means. Maybe something will happen that will liberate me from your clutches, so I don't have to produce your boring designs and don't end up bankrupt paying your money back, either!'

A miracle, she was thinking. Maybe she'd win the pools or walk off with first prize in the national lottery!

Vass did not answer. He gave her a long look. Then he waved one hand towards the door, dismissing her. 'Have some sketches on my desk by the end of next week,' he commanded. 'And this time, my dear Lisa, make sure they're suitable.'

Classic was what he wanted. Continuity was what he demanded. OK, Lisa decided furiously. That's what I'll give him!

For most of the week she'd been seated at her desk, wading through piles of old G.W. design books, taking notes, making sketches, dashing off diagrams, in an effort to come up with some common thread in the mish-mash of styles that dragged dully across the pages.

It was a mind-boggling task. It was making her crazy. It was like looking for a matchstick in a forest.

The designs were all unremittingly tedious, devoid of flair, totally uninspiring. How could she produce anything that bore the stamp of continuity and at the same time managed to be fresh and original?

She sighed and continued to turn the pages. The task she'd been given was quite unachievable. If Vass wanted bonfires, here was his material!

And yet. . .and yet. . .as she continued to rough out sketches, almost in spite of herself, something was taking shape inside her head.

There *was* a common thread there, something she could utilise. Suddenly the ideas were flowing.

By late afternoon there was a pile of sketches on her desk. She glanced through them quickly. But they were rough. They needed polishing before she subjected them to Alexander Vass's scrutiny. She pulled a fresh pile of paper from her desk drawer, sharpened her pencil and got down to work.

Lisa was scarcely aware of all the other staff leaving. She had glanced up briefly as Kerry, one of her assistants, approached her. 'It's half-past five. Everybody's gone. It's time you were packing up your things.'

'I won't be long now.' Lisa had glanced at her watch. 'I just have a couple of things to finish. I have to show them to Mr Vass before he leaves.'

'He's already left. An unexpected appointment.' Kerry smiled. 'Don't you remember, his secretary came round earlier to tell us?'

Lisa did vaguely remember, now that Kerry mentioned it, but she'd been so absorbed in what she was doing at the time that she hadn't really paid a great deal of attention.

'Finish what you're doing tomorrow,' Kerry urged her. 'Go home. You look as though you need a rest.'

Lisa felt touched by the girl's unexpected kindness. Out of all her workmates, Kerry was possibly the least friendly, which made her current show of concern all the more special.

She smiled up at her now. 'I think you're right. It's time I called it a day. I feel utterly whacked.'

But as Kerry bade her goodnight Lisa had decided to take the sketches home and finish them there. After all, she was going to be alone this evening. Emily, as a special treat, was staying over at a school-friend's. Instead of ironing, as she'd planned, she'd spend the evening with her sketchpad. The ironing would just have to wait!

The little house seemed strange and empty without Emily. How she hated it when her daughter wasn't there! As Lisa popped a breast of chicken into the microwave she glanced at the brightly coloured childish drawings secured by fruit-shaped magnets to the fridge door and her heart turned over with maternal pride. What a gifted, talented child her daughter was!

For some reason these thoughts of Emily sent her memory shooting back to the previous Friday in Vass's office when he had brought up the subject of the new crèche and she had somehow ended up, almost aggressively, informing him that it was not her intention, ever, to remarry.

She'd wondered then why she'd done that, and why, quite deliberately, she'd encouraged another false notion of his—his belief that, secretly, she was still mourning Tony.

A frown touched her brow to recall the feeling of unease that had gripped her during that brief conversation. She'd felt strangely vulnerable, half afraid, overcome by a mass of conflicting emotions.

Fool! she chastised herself, giving herself a shake as the buzzer on the microwave announced that the chicken was ready. Why was she upsetting herself with thoughts of Vass? Pulling the oven door open, she chased away all thoughts of him. She would not allow him to spoil her evening!

The chicken was delicious, and Lisa was feeling revitalised as she made herself some coffee and settled down to work. She'd phoned Emily's school chum's mother while the coffee was perking and received a report that everything was fine. Now, her mind at rest, she could get back to her sketches.

Just after ten her task was completed. Lisa leaned back in her chair with a warm sense of achievement and, yawning, stretched her arms above her head. A warm bath to soothe her tense, tired muscles, she decided, then she'd curl up in bed for an hour with a book.

She got as far as the bathroom and was half undressed when the doorbell rang, making her start.

Who could it be at this hour? She reached for her dressing-gown. None of her friends would call round this late.

As the bell rang again, insistently, urgently, she headed for the door, pulling the dressing-gown around her, feeling a cold spring of fear welling up inside.

Emily! Her heart thudded. Had something happened to Emily?

She pulled the door open, suddenly terrified of finding a solemn-faced policeman standing there, come to give her some terrible news.

But her visitor was no policeman. Relief and anger swept through her as she looked up into the familiar dark, scowling face.

Alexander Vass did not wait for an invitation. He strode past her into the hall. 'I want a word with you!' he thundered.

CHAPTER SIX

LISA whirled round to face him. 'What the hell's going on here? What do you mean by barging into my house?'

Alexander Vass flung her a look of pure contempt. 'It didn't work. We caught it in time. You might have saved yourself the bother.'

'What bother? What didn't work? What are you talking about?' The anger in his face was shocking, almost frightening. The dark eyes seemed to flay her alive.

'Don't lie to me, Lisa!' He took a step towards her, as though he might grab hold of her and squeeze the life from her body. But he did not lay a hand on her. He simply growled in fury, 'In spite of all your threats, I didn't believe you'd actually do something. It never occurred to me that you could be this spiteful.'

'Do what? What are you talking about?' Lisa was shouting now as she confronted, with a growing sense of frustration, the tall dark figure in the navy cashmere overcoat. 'Stop talking in riddles and explain what's going on!'

He did grab her then, firmly, by the elbow. 'You know what's going on! You know exactly what I'm talking about! Don't try and play the innocent with me!'

For an instant her heart skittered like a pebble over water as he pulled her towards him, his fingers hard against her flesh. And something stilled within her as in that instant she caught a tantalising waft of the rich, dark scent of him and felt the hard, powerful warmth of him press against her.

But this time that feeling of being overpowered, which, in the past, she had been so helplessly prey to, was itself overcome by raw indignation. She tugged her arm furiously. 'Let me go! This minute! What the hell do you think you're up to? Have you taken leave of your senses?'

Vass did not release her. His grip simply hardened. 'You're a liar! A little cheat! But then, I always knew that! And now I discover you're an arsonist as well!'

Uttering that final rough accusation, he released her, thrusting her from him as though she were unclean.

Lisa staggered, disoriented. He *had* gone crazy! Arson? What the devil was he talking about?

She opened her mouth to demand an explanation, but he was swinging away from her, heading for the sitting-room. 'I need a drink,' he muttered beneath his breath.

'Just a minute!' Lisa strode, barefoot, after him. 'Before you do another thing, kindly explain to me in plain simple English why you're here and what you're talking about. I believe you said something a moment ago about arson.' She stood in the doorway, arms folded across her chest. 'You can start off by explaining that.'

He had turned to look at her, slipping off his coat as he did so and tossing it carelessly over the back of one of the armchairs. He said, ignoring her demand, 'Where do you keep the brandy?'

Lisa glared into his face and remained motionless in the doorway. If she had been angry before, she was twice as angry now. His arrogance almost took her breath away.

Her gaze did not waver. 'I'm waiting for an explanation.'

Vass looked back at her. 'I don't think you need an explanation. Now, where did you say you keep your brandy?'

As she stood there, heart racing, just for a moment Lisa did not trust herself to answer him. If I open my mouth I'll end up screaming, she was thinking. If I allow myself to move one single muscle I shall walk across that floor and tear him apart.

Vass regarded her flushed face, then let his eyes drift slowly down the length of her slender, dressing-gown-clad figure. He smiled, making her suddenly feel oddly vulnerable. 'Did I catch you on your way to bed?'

Lisa felt her flesh burn beneath the thin towelling fabric. His eyes seemed to be stripping the robe from her shoulders, peeling it away, fold by fold, to leave her standing there before him, naked and raw.

She kept a firm grip on her voice, concealing her sudden confusion, as she responded stubbornly, 'I'm still waiting for an explanation.'

'And I'm still waiting for my brandy.' He even had the cheek to smile as he said it.

'Then you'll wait forever. I don't keep brandy. I'm afraid my budget doesn't stretch to such luxuries.'

He raised one dark eyebrow. 'Whisky, then? Beer?'

'I'm afraid not.' Lisa nodded in the direction of the

kitchen. 'If you're thirsty there's plenty of water in the tap.'

Alexander Vass remained standing by the armchair. 'Are you always such a hospitable hostess? Is water the best you have to offer your guests?'

'You're not my guest. I didn't invite you here.' Yet the rebuke had raised a flush to her cheeks. She relented a fraction. 'I'll make you tea, if you want.'

'No, thanks, a glass of water will do me perfectly. I wouldn't wish to put you to any trouble.' He turned with a wry smile and headed for the kitchen. 'Look. I'll even fetch it myself.'

Lisa scowled at his back as he disappeared through the doorway, hating the ambivalence of the feelings that churned inside her. He had barged into her house with the sole purpose of making trouble and she felt resentful and furious about that. She also felt confused—and not only about what he was doing here. What confused her even more was that her resentment and her anger were offset by an indefinable sense of excitement at his presence. And, to add to that, he had even succeeded in making her feel guilty for her lack of hospitality!

She stepped into the room and went to stand by the armchair where he had so carelessly thrown his coat. And as she stood there, listening to the sounds coming from the kitchen, of glasses clinking and water splashing, she found herself glancing down at his coat.

Its rich, soft folds contrasted sharply with the worn, shabby fabric of the armchair, the delicate sheen of purest cashmere against the threadbare roughness of ancient cotton.

It was a parable of their relationship, Lisa thought, her anger sharpening, dousing that treacherous sensation of excitment. He had it all. She was poor, she had nothing. And yet, as carelessly as he had discarded this coat, he had deliberately destroyed her hopes and her dreams. It was shameful when he could so easily have afforded to show compassion.

At that moment he reappeared in the kitchen doorway and, seeming not to see the censure in her eyes, or not to care, observed with a dry smile, holding aloft his glass of water, 'Handy stuff for putting out fires.'

'Which brings us neatly back to my question.' Lisa watched with irritation as he came into the room, pushed aside his coat and sat down in the armchair. 'What was that accusation of arson supposed to mean?'

Vass took a mouthful of his water. 'So, you still claim you don't know what I'm talking about? Quite frankly, I find that a little difficult to swallow.'

She was going round in circles. A cat chasing its own tail. Perhaps if she asked him a simple, straightforward question she would receive a simple, straightforward answer in return.

Lisa looked him in the eye. She had stepped away from the armchair to stand by the coffee-table in the centre of the room. 'Has there,' she demanded, 'been a fire?'

'Yes, there's been a fire.'

'At the factory?'

'At the factory.'

'Bad?'

'Not too bad. Fortunately it was caught in time. One of the residents of the flats that overlook the factory saw the flames and phoned the fire brigade. Only the fabrics store-room has been slightly damaged.'

'And you think I did it? You must be seriously crazy if you're capable of believing a thing like that.'

Vass laid down his glass. 'You're the obvious suspect. You hate me. You resent our working arrangement.' He paused. 'And, most significantly, you have made threats.'

'They weren't serious threats! I was simply angry!'

'And angry people do angry things.'

'Maybe so, but it wasn't me!'

'Can you prove it? Where have you been for the past four hours?'

'Right here in this house.' She resisted adding that she had been working overtime on his designs. 'I got back about six-thirty and I haven't been out again.'

He eyed her. 'Have you an alibi? Your daughter, for example? Can she support this claim of yours?'

Lisa frowned. 'No, she can't. In fact, nobody can. I've been on my own the entire evening.' In spite of herself, she felt a small flicker of alarm. His sudden talk of alibis made the whole thing sound serious.

Vass regarded her suspiciously. 'Isn't that unusual? I mean, for your daughter to be away?'

She could not deny it. 'Yes, it is unusual. But it just happened to be her best friend's birthday and she was invited to a special birthday tea and to stay overnight.'

'How very convenient.' The dark eyes pierced her. 'No wonder you chose this evening to act.'

'You're talking nonsense! Utter nonsense! The only reason you believe that is because you want to!'

'And because of the points I mentioned earlier. You

had the motivation, a reason to get back at me. Didn't you say yourself that you intended finding a way to put an end to our arrangement? Burning down the factory would have been a pretty foolproof method.'

'A little drastic, however. Not my style.'

'No? On the contrary, it seems to me that such a drastic gesture would fit well with your character. You are an impetuous young woman, given to bold, dramatic gestures.'

There was some truth in that. Her Arien nature was impetuous. But his insight irked her. Lisa glared into his face. 'I may be, to some extent. But I'm not a criminal.'

'Plus,' he continued, ignoring her protest, 'you have no alibi, as you've just confessed. And, what's more, you were reportedly the last member of staff to leave the premises this evening. For some unexplained reason you were still lurking about at a time when, normally, you would long since have gone home.'

'I was working late! I wasn't lurking about!' What else, she wondered irritably, did he know about her movements? And who had told him that she'd stayed late at the office? The only person it could have been was Kerry.

But that was not important. She dismissed the query as another, far more pertinent thought popped into her head. She squared her shoulders. 'May I draw your attention to a somewhat crucial oversight on your part?'

'Meaning?'

'Meaning. . .' Lisa smiled back at him triumphantly. This time, for once, she was one step ahead of him.

'Meaning,' she continued, 'that your neat little theory that I'm the obvious suspect is actually pretty hollow. . .'

As he raised a curious eyebrow she elaborated with satisfaction, 'I can think of someone far more likely to have put a torch to G.W. Fashions than myself.'

'Oh, yes?'

He was waiting for her revelation. She felt a warm sense of power as she kept him dangling for a moment. 'Much, much more likely than myself,' she emphasised, taking pleasure in spinning out her moment of triumph. She smiled an arch smile and slid her hands into her pockets. 'Nigel, the designer you fired to make room for me.'

As Vass watched her, saying nothing, Lisa hurried on, 'Someone whom you have unfairly deprived of a job is far more likely, I would have thought, to be out looking for revenge.'

Vass nodded, seeming to consider her allegation. Then he smiled a crushing smile. 'That's what I thought,' he told her. 'That's why I immediately gave his name to the police.' As Lisa's face fell he continued, 'However, it would seem that poor, downtrodden Nigel has what they call a cast-iron alibi. He was at the pub with some friends all evening. There are at least a dozen people who can testify to that.

'So, you see,' he concluded, 'that brings us back to you. And you, unlike poor old Nigel, have no alibi, it seems.'

He was so lacking in compassion, in basic humanity. Not only was he enjoying trying to blame the fire on Lisa, when surely he must know she had enough problems already, but that reference to 'poor, down-trodden Nigel' was almost shocking in its coldness. He didn't care that he had deprived the poor man of his livelihood. He simply didn't care for anyone at all.

Her voice tight with the renewed surge of dislike she felt for him, Lisa demanded, 'So, if I'm the prime suspect, what are you doing here? Why haven't the police come instead to drag me off in chains?'

Alexander Vass leaned back in his armchair. 'Why don't you sit down instead of hovering about there?' He waved at the other armchair. 'Make yourself at home.'

Lisa's hands balled into fists in her dressing-gown pockets. His arrogance knew no limits. She felt like punching him.

She said as evenly as her angrily clenched teeth would allow her, 'I feel like standing, so I'll stand, if you don't mind. Kindly don't presume to issue me orders in my own house.'

'No such presumption was intended.' Vass smiled that fleeting, luminous smile of his that never failed to throw Lisa off balance. It seemed to come from nowhere, it transformed him utterly and it invariably caused her anger against him to feel quite suddenly totally inappropriate.

Oh, he was definitely a Cancer! He waxed and waned like the moon!

His gaze flickered across her face, amused and arrogant. 'It's just that you look so awkward standing there.'

'Thank you for your concern, but I don't feel awkward in the slightest. I feel, as it so happens, perfectly comfortable.'

Yet, as she said it, she withdrew her hands from her pockets and folded them firmly over her chest. She did feel awkward, though not physically, but spiritually. There was something a little unsettling about this shifting quality of his—this ability, like a prism, to cast lights of varying colours, all different, all startling, all totally unexpected. One never quite knew which side he'd show next.

Though there was one side to him that was irritatingly consistent. The wretched man never answered her questions!

She scowled at him. 'Perhaps you didn't hear me. . .I asked you what you were doing here. . .why you didn't send the police. . .'

Vass regarded her for a moment. The dark eyes narrowed. 'The reason the police haven't come to question you is that I haven't told them about my suspicions.'

There was a moment of silence while Lisa took in this frankly astonishing piece of information. 'Why ever not?' she queried, bewildered. 'Surely you'd feel much safer with me locked behind bars?'

He did not smile at her wry humour. He laid his hands on the chair arms. 'Perhaps it was unwise of me to keep my suspicions to myself. No doubt I shall find that out in good time.' He paused, looking hard at her. 'But I had a very good reason. . .'

Lisa was actually naïve enough, just for a moment, to allow the possibility to creep into her mind that he had kept silent in order to protect her. Not that she needed protecting. She was innocent of the charge. But he, misguidedly, quite clearly believed otherwise.

But what he was protecting was not her at all. What he was protecting, predictably, were his own interests.

He told her plainly, 'My reason was this: I have no wish to lose my newly appointed designer at such a crucial stage in the proceedings. With the spring shows only a couple of months away, it would be impossible for me to appoint a replacement who could get a collection ready in time.' He smiled at her thinly. 'Unfortunately, I need you. It's as simple as that. As much as I would like to hand you over to the police, I have no choice but to keep my suspicions to myself.'

He smiled without humour. 'I shall, however, be keeping an even closer eye on you in future.'

'That won't be necessary.' She said it without conviction. She could see in his eyes that he would not be won over. Then she peered at him over the barrier of her firmly folded arms and expressed a thought that had occurred to her before, but that now she felt impress itself on her even more strongly. 'It's important to you, isn't it, this move into the world of fashion? You really want it to succeed?'

He stretched out his long legs and crossed them at the ankles. 'Naturally, I want it to succeed. Why should you be so surprised about that?'

He was right. She *was* surprised. She answered, watching him, 'Of course, it's only natural that you should want it to succeed. But it's *how much* you care about it that really surprises me. After all,' she added as he looked back at her impassively, 'it accounts for only a fraction of your business interests. I imagine that Silver Star Navigation makes more money for you in one afternoon that G.W. Fashions is likely to make in a year.'

Vass smiled at that. 'That's not a bad estimate. Perhaps a trifle optimistic as regards Silver Star.'

'But it means that if G.W. Fashions folded it wouldn't actually be crucial to you financially. It would be no more than an unfortunate, but barely noticeable, little blip.'

'I suppose that's true.'

'So why are you bothering? Why are you going to so much trouble to ensure that it succeeds?'

Vass spread his long fingers over the chair arms and seemed to contemplate them for a moment. 'Perhaps,' he said at last, 'I don't like to be beaten.'

Lisa did not doubt that. 'I'm sure you don't.' But she sensed all the same that there was more to it than that. As he glanced up at her, his eyes shuttered, she found herself asking another question that had been puzzling her for a while.

'But why take up the challenge in the first place? Why take on an unprofitable company, in a line of business so far removed from shipping, that's going to demand so much of your time?'

'Perhaps I want to diversify?'

'But why pick fashion? Why pick an area that's totally alien to you, an area with which you have no links at all?'

Alexander Vass did not answer immediately. He glanced down once again at his long tanned fingers. And for once Lisa managed to suppress her irritation and bit back the impatient demand for an answer that she felt instinctively rising to her lips. He was about to tell her something. She could sense it.

At last he looked up at her. 'Perhaps you are mistaken. Perhaps there are links of which you are unaware.'

'Are there?' Lisa's tone had softened. Suddenly she was curious. And he was on the brink, she sensed, of surprising her with a confidence.

He let his eyes roam her face, as though he was assessing her worthiness as a repository for his secrets. Then he said quite simply, 'My grandfather was a tailor. A simple tailor who spent most of his life working in a sweat-shop in the East End of London.' A wry smile touched his lips. 'A common enough fate for a penniless immigrant in those days.'

'Penniless immigrant?' Lisa blinked at him. 'Your grandfather was a penniless immigrant?'

'I see you're surprised. What did you think? That I was born with a silver spoon in my mouth?'

That was exactly what she had thought. Or rather she had assumed it without thinking. Suddenly she felt ashamed, oddly narrow-minded.

With a small sigh that sounded distinctly apologetic, she sank down on the edge of the armchair opposite him. 'I had no idea. You give the impression of a man who has been accustomed all his life to wealth and privilege.'

Vass laughed. 'I wish my grandfather could hear you. I'm sure he would find that highly amusing.' Then he continued, a note of real warmth in his voice, 'My grandfather was born in Greece, in the slums of Athens, where he trained to be a tailor. He came here with my grandmother when he was in his early twenties, changed his name from Vassilakas to Vass and found himself a job in the only trade he knew.

'They had one son, my father, who, along with my mother, died in an accident when I was just a baby. It was my grandparents who raised me, who gave me an education, who made it possible through their sacrifices to become what I am today.'

There was pride in his voice, gratitude and humility. Lisa looked back at him, moved and distinctly chastened. She said, 'Are your grandparents still alive?'

He nodded. 'Very much so. And enjoying their retirement in a beautiful villa on the island of Skiros. A token of my eternal gratitude and love.'

Something twisted inside her at the naked emotion that flashed for a moment across his face. So he was human, after all. Deeply human. She found the revelation unexpectedly disturbing.

'So, you see, I have very strong links with the fashion business—namely my grandfather and the sweat-shop where he spent thirty years of his life. For that little sweat-shop in the East End of London is where, believe it or not, G.W. Fashions started.'

As her eyes widened he added, 'Perhaps now you can understand the reason why I bought it and why it is so important to me that it should succeed?'

'You're doing it for your grandfather? To vindicate his years of sacrifice?' It was not really a question. Of course she understood.

'So now you also know why I intend to hang on to you? So far, alas, you have failed to deliver, but I know you're capable of producing the designs that can turn G.W. Fashions' fortunes around.'

As he held her eyes a moment fingers of warmth spread through her. She felt oddly pleased and flattered by the compliment. To her own mild astonishment she murmured, 'I'll try.'

'Good girl. I know that you can do it.'

Lisa held her breath. 'And I didn't start the fire.'

The dark eyes still lingered. 'Well, let's hope that's the end of it.' His tone was without menace, but Lisa sensed he did not believe her. Then he stood up slowly. 'I'd better go now.' He paused and smiled that quick, bright smile of his. 'I apologise for keeping you out of bed.'

'That doesn't matter.' Lisa's heart was thumping strangely as he reached for his coat and quickly slipped it on. And all she could think of, as she rose to her feet and politely accompanied him to the front door, was that, suddenly, she did not want him to leave.

Perhaps he had read her mind. He turned to face her in the doorway. 'Thank you for the water.' His eyes were smiling. Then he reached out one hand and touched her cheek softly. 'Goodnight, Lisa. I'll see you tomorrow.'

'Goodni——' But she stumbled over the final syllable, for suddenly his dark head was leaning towards her and she felt his lips lightly brush against her cheek.

It was so quick, so unexpected, that it took her breath away. Yet the reaction within her was instant and ferocious. A vast powerful longing suddenly overwhelmed her.

With a foolish sense of loss she stood and watched as he hurried down the path towards the waiting Bentley. More than anything in the world she had wanted him to stay.

CHAPTER SEVEN

THESE feelings, Lisa decided later, were easily explained away.

The reason she'd been so reluctant for Alexander Vass to leave had had nothing to do with the man himself. How could it, she told herself, when she didn't even like him? What had prompted the feeling had been the story he'd told her about his grandfather and his link with G.W. Fashions. It was a fascinating story. She'd longed to hear more of it. It was the story, not the story-teller, that had mesmerised her.

Lisa was up early next morning and on the phone to Emily, anxious to speak to her daughter before she went off to school. 'I'll see you this evening, sweetheart,' she told her. 'Be a good girl and be sure to thank Cindy's mother for giving you such a lovely time.'

She laid down the phone with a small sigh of relief. The thought of seeing Emily again made her feel better. She missed her so dreadfully when she was away, as though a part of her very own body was missing.

Inwardly she frowned. More than likely, Emily's absence last night had been part of the reason that she had reacted so ridiculously to Alexander Vass. She hadn't been herself. She'd been feeling lonely and vulnerable. She nodded. That was it. That had to be the reason. So now the entire silly episode had been fully accounted for!

The whole place was buzzing when she arrived at work that morning. Everyone was talking about the fire.

'What a thing to have happened!' Kerry exclaimed as Lisa joined the other members of staff in the fabrics store-room to have a look at the damage. 'Who could've done such a terrible thing?'

'I can't imagine. It really is dreadful.' Feeling the girl's eyes on her, Lisa fought back a blush. Did Kerry know that she, Lisa, was under suspicion? Probably not, she decided with a sense of quick relief. After all, Vass was keeping that suspicion to himself.

As Vass had told her last night, the damage wasn't too bad. A couple of dozen bales of fabric had been destroyed, partly by the fire and partly by the water that had been used by the fire brigade to put the fire out. The ceiling and the walls in places were badly scorched, but structurally there had been very little damage and, luckily, the fire had been brought under control before it had had time to spread to other parts of the building.

'Disappointing, huh?'

As a low voice spoke behind her Lisa jumped, startled, and swung round quickly to face the speaker. She had known it was Vass, of course. She'd recognised his voice. She'd know that deep bear-like growl of his anywhere!

But, all the same, her heart jumped disconcertingly. Before her eyes arose a memory of how he had looked at her last night.

He was not, however, looking at her in such a way now. His features were expressionless, devoid of warmth or softness. Lisa looked back at him levelly. 'Disappointed? Why should I be? I don't like to see destruction and waste.'

He ignored her disavowal. 'As you can see, the damage is minimal. Our arsonist, I'm afraid, didn't do a very good job.'

'No, they didn't. I would say it's a pretty poor effort—at least, if it was their intention to burn the place down.'

'I think that was their intention.'

'If you say so.'

'The police know for a fact that it was started deliberately.'

'Then perhaps they'll discover soon who the guilty party is.'

'Is that what you're hoping—or are you hoping the opposite? That the guilty party will remain undetected?'

Lisa smiled a small smile and treated him to a taste of the kind of evasiveness of which he himself was such a master. 'As a good and faithful employee, I'm hoping, Mr Vass, for the outcome that will cause least inconvenience to yourself.'

Vass held her eyes. 'Of course,' he answered. He smiled cynically. 'Your fidelity is duly noted.' Then he stepped away from her to address the other members of staff, who were still standing in curious groups, discussing the damage.

'I think we've all seen enough now, ladies and gentlemen. I thank you for your concern. Perhaps we can all get back to work now? I shall keep you abreast of any developments.'

He turned back to Lisa. 'I'd like to see you in my office.' Then he swung round and marched off through the door.

Lisa threw a scowl after him. He was so damned peremptory! How he enjoyed snapping his fingers!

A couple of minutes later, however, she was tapping at his door, then pushing it open as he bade her, 'Come in!'

She stepped up to his desk, as he continued flicking through some papers, and fixed her eyes on the top of his arrogant head. 'I believe you wished to see me, Mr Vass?'

He waved to one of the chairs, without glancing up at her. 'Make yourself comfortable. I'll be with you in a moment.'

Lisa sat, her hands folded patiently in her lap. How could she have softened towards him last night? she was thinking. Truly, she must have been out of her mind!

Idly she let her eyes drift over his desk, over the orderly piles of papers and files arranged there. And that was when, suddenly, something caught her eye.

A large colourful greetings card, propped in one corner, skewed slightly, so that, if she craned her neck slightly, she could read the message written inside.

Lisa craned her neck slightly, crushing her sense of horror at this display of bad-mannered curiosity. And, as she read the words, written in a flowing feminine hand, the oddest sensation went lurching through her.

'To darling Alexander,' was the message. 'Wishing

you lots of luck in your new venture. All my love always. From your dearest Nina.'

Lisa snatched her eyes away. How touching, she thought cynically. His lady-love obviously cares a lot about him. But beneath the careful cynicism she was aware of another, less comfortable, emotion stirring inside her.

It was gone in an instant as at last he looked up at her and pushed aside the papers he'd been leafing through. He sat back in his chair. 'I think you know why I wish to see you. As I'm sure you remember, I issued a deadline for your production of some new sketches.' His eyes hardened. 'That deadline has now expired.'

Darling Alexander! It was a contradiction in terms, Lisa found herself thinking as she looked back across the desk at him. Whoever his dearest Nina was, she must have had a hard time of it!

She shook the thought from her and answered, 'Yes, I'm aware of that.'

'So?' His eyebrows lifted. 'What is your excuse?'

'I have no excuse.'

The eyebrows lifted higher. 'If I may say so, that's not like you in the slightest.'

'If I may say so. . .' Lisa looked back at him unflinchingly '. . .you weren't here yesterday evening when the deadline under discussion expired.'

'That only makes things worse—from your point of view. In effect, my absence provided you with extra time. So, if that's your excuse, I'm afraid it's a pretty lame one.'

'I've already told you I have no excuse.' Lisa paused

a moment, watching his expression darken. Then she smiled a cool smile. 'You see, I have no need of excuses.' She bent down quickly and retrieved the folder that, as she'd sat down, she'd laid on the floor by her chair. 'As it happens, Mr Vass, I have the sketches right here. They were ready last night, in time for your deadline. I simply used the extra time to polish them a little.'

She had expected him to be annoyed at the way she had played him along. This reversal of roles, she had sensed, would irk him. But, to her surprise, he smiled broadly. 'OK, I deserved that. I made the wrong assumption. I should have given you the benefit of the doubt.'

Lisa hid her surprise—and her sense of irritation. For some perverse reason she had wanted him to be annoyed. She had not wanted him to respond with a show of good humour. She had not wanted him to behave like 'darling Alexander'!

She said, aware that her tone was unnecessarily clipped, 'Yes, indeed you should. You really ought to know that I'm not the sort of person who fails to meet deadlines in her work.'

As he looked back at her she wished she hadn't said that. The remark had been intended to put him in his place, but it had come out sounding peevish and sensitive, as though she actually gave a damn about what he thought of her. And nothing could be further from the truth.

But he hadn't even noticed. He was leaning across the desk towards her. 'Let me see the sketches,' he demanded.

Lisa flicked open the folder and carefully slipped out
her sketches. Then she half stood up to lay them before
him. Suddenly, unexpectedly, she felt nervous.

He took his time about going through them, exam-
ining each one individually, making no comments,
keeping her in suspense, as she perched apprehensively
on the edge of her chair.

Then at last he looked up. 'Congratulations,' he told
her. 'I really think you've got something here.'

Lisa flushed with pleasure, hating herself for doing
it. His opinion of her work, like his opinion of her as a
person, really shouldn't matter to her in the slightest.
But, before she could stop herself, she was leaning
forward and pointing to a couple of the sketches in
particular.

'That basic shape—the squarish shoulders and
narrow hips—is one that I discovered, when I went
through the files, keeps turning up again and again
over the years. It's almost like a G.W. Fashions
hallmark—though hard to recognise at times because
of the fussy way it's been handled.

'As you can see, I've simplified it and brought it up
to date. . .That coat, that dress. . .they're good
examples. They're modern, yet they have a distinct
hint of that classic flavour you're after.'

It was as she came to the end of her enthusiastic
little speech that she realised she was leaning halfway
across his desk, so close that she could almost have
counted his lashes and the tiny fine lines around the
corners of his mouth.

Abruptly she sat down again and struggled to control

the sudden erratic pounding of her heart. 'I think these are what you're after,' she concluded lamely.

Alexander Vass sat back in his chair again. 'I can see you've been busy, and, as I said, I congratulate you. These are a vast improvement on the others.'

'I'm glad you like them.' Her heart was still beating strangely, and she had the distinct and humiliating sensation that Vass was aware of this shameful condition. As though he could see beneath her skin with those piercing dark eyes of his to the anguished pulsing ball that was her heart at this moment.

He smiled, she thought, a trifle condescendingly. 'As I said, on the whole I think they're perfect. . .But there's still a handful that are not quite suitable. . .'

A sense of disappointment, quite out of proportion, went slamming through her, making her cheeks pale. She said in a strained voice, 'What makes you say that? You see, I think they're all perfectly suitable.'

'I can appreciate that you do, and I don't mean to sound critical. But there are just a couple that——'

'Just a couple that what?' Angrily she cut in before he could finish. Her tone was sharp, seething with anger. And, though she knew she was over-reacting, she couldn't help it. 'What's wrong with them?' she demanded, suddenly all fiery Arien. 'Go on, tell me! I want to know!'

To Lisa's surprise, Vass smiled an amused smile. He leaned back in his seat. 'My, but we're touchy. Are you always this touchy about your work?'

The answer to that was no. She was sensitive, but not this touchy. Criticism had never triggered an explosion like this before. She looked back at Vass, feeling faintly foolish, wondering what had caused it to happen now.

But he was one step ahead of her. 'But then, you're touchy about everything. At least, you're touchy about everything with me.'

'I don't think that's so.' She did not like that accusation.

But he insisted. 'Oh, but you are. Extremely so.'

Lisa snatched her gaze away. Was she really? As much as she hated it, the accusation struck a chord. She looked back at him. 'Then that must be because you provoke me. Because you're always trying to get the better of me. I don't like people attacking me all the time.'

'Attacking you?' His eyebrows rose. 'When have I ever attacked you? You're the one, I would say, who goes in for aggression.'

Was he referring to the damage she had inflicted on his car? To the fire he believed she had started at the factory? To the time she had thrown the copies of the contract across the desk at him?

In spite of herself, Lisa smiled a wry smile. It was quite a litany of aggression, even though on at least one count she was entirely innocent! She looked across at him and told him frankly, 'I fear you simply bring out the worst in me.'

'I wonder why that is?'

'Because we're opposites. Chalk and cheese.' Fire and water, she might have added. 'And opposites often have that effect on one another.'

'I suppose that's true.' For a moment he sat watching her, an oddly intense look in those dark probing eyes of his. Then the dark eyes seemed to darken. 'But they can also attract.'

It was the oddest sensation. As though he had reached out and touched her. Lisa felt her heart skip a beat inside her. She felt oddly revealed. Unmasked. Caught out.

She said, 'So they say.'

'And do you think it's true?'

'It might be. In some cases.' Was he making fun of her? After all, she had suspected for a long time now that he was aware of the effect he sometimes had on her.

'In some cases, but not in all? Is that what you're saying?'

'Definitely not in all.' She swallowed quickly. She forced a weak smile. 'Look at us, for example.'

'Indeed.' He was watching her, letting his gaze travel over her, apparently enoying this provocative exchange and the fact that he had brought a faint blush to her cheeks.

She felt a needle of annoyance goading her to retaliate. With a cool look, and willing herself not to glance at the greetings card, Lisa reminded him, 'But that's no loss to either of us. After all, as you yourself were at pains to point out to me, you're already well supplied with lovers.'

That was not strictly accurate, that use of the plural. All he had said was that his love-life was being well taken care of—and it was perfectly clear from the tenor of her greeting that Nina believed herself to be in the singular.

But Lisa, without ever actually consciously thinking

about it, had always assumed there must be more than
one woman in his life. Her use of the plural was almost
a kind of challenge. For some silly reason she was
curious to know the truth.

Vass, predictably, did not rise to her challenge.
Instead he simply laughed, showing perfect white teeth.
'Certainly, I have no complaints in that department.'
Then he looked her in the eye. 'And what about you?
Do you have a man in your life?'

'I don't need a man. I have my daughter.' Lisa's tone
was somewhat sharper than it need have been. All at
once she was annoyed with her own foolish curiosity.
What did it matter to her if he had one special woman
or a harem? What on earth kind of madness had that
greetings card stirred in her?

She threw him a cool look. 'My daughter's more
than enough for me.'

'It's a lot, a child, I'll grant you.' As he had looked
at her Vass's expression had sobered. 'But are you
really sure that it's enough?'

What was he getting at? What was he leading her
into? Whatever it was, Lisa did not want to know.

She tilted her chin at him. 'I have my daughter and I
have my work. Take my word for it, I'm totally
satisfied.' Then, touched by a strange panic, she took a
deep breath and grabbed the opportunity to change the
subject.

'Talking about work, as we were just a moment
ago. . .perhaps you wouldn't mind explaining to me
why you want to reject some of the new designs I've
just shown you?'

Vass continued to look at her, dark eyes scrutinising,

unhurriedly sweeping over her face. Lisa wondered for a moment what he was thinking and whether he was about to shift the direction of the conversation back again. But, instead, he put to her calmly, 'Who said I was rejecting them?'

Did he take her for a fool? Lisa straightened defensively. 'It sounded remarkably like rejection to me. Correct me if I'm wrong, but I distinctly heard you say that some of my designs weren't quite suitable.'

Vass nodded. 'And, if you'd given me the chance to finish, you would also have heard me specify "for the general collection". I have no intention whatsoever of rejecting any of the designs that you've just shown me.'

Lisa frowned. 'What are you saying?'

'What I'm saying is this: there are a handful of your new designs that I think are too special to be included in the general collection.'

'And?' Her heart was beating.

'And what I propose is this—that we introduce an additional label into the collection. Lisa's Special Collection. Call it what you will. Designed to attract a younger, bolder market.'

'You mean you want to use them? You're not rejecting them?'

He laughed. 'On the contrary, I plan to give them special status. That is, if you like the idea.'

How could she not like it? 'It's a terrific idea!' Suddenly Lisa was grinning from ear to ear. And suddenly, too, her brain was whirring. 'I'll do some additional designs for the special collection. We'll need a few more to fill it out.'

Vass shrugged. 'That's up to you. If you think you can manage it.'

'Oh, I can manage it!' Lisa beamed confidently as Vass gathered up her sketches and handed them back to her. 'I love the idea. I can't wait to get started!'

Five minutes later she was back at her desk, fired with enthusiasm, busily sketching.

But, in spite of the genuine excitement that possessed her, she could not quite banish from her mind a picture of that greetings card, signed 'From your dearest Nina', that stood propped in one corner of Vass's desk.

The next three weeks were one long, continuous workday, weekdays and weekends merging together, one day seeming to flow into the next.

But she had made huge progress, Lisa congratulated herself as she got ready to pack up at the end of another exhausting day. A few of the garments were already completed and locked away safely in a cupboard. And she was enormously pleased with them. They did her great credit.

She leaned back in her chair and stretched her arms above her head. With each day that passed she became more deeply involved and more enthusiastic about what she was doing. It was undoubtedly the most exciting job she'd ever done.

And her brain was constantly a-buzz with ideas. Tonight, for example, after Emily was in bed, she'd get down to work on some of her designs for accessories. She already had a couple of good ideas.

She yawned. Maybe tonight she could get to bed by midnight!

'I think what you need, young lady, is a rest.'

Lisa whirled round, startled, at the sound of Vass's voice. He was walking across the office floor towards her. For some silly reason she felt her heart jump inside her.

Averting her head, she bent down quickly and finished stuffing some sheets of paper and pencils into a plastic bag. But she could feel his eyes on her, a prickling sensation.

'I'm just leaving,' she told him. 'I was just packing up.'

'But not planning for much of a rest,' he observed quietly, glancing at the bulging plastic bag. 'Don't you do anything but work these days?'

'Sure I do. I eat. I sleep.' She was deliberately offhand. There was an odd note in his voice, as though he was suggesting she had taken on too much. She could not have borne it if he were suddenly to change his mind and demand that she give the whole thing up.

'I think you need a break.' He had stepped right up to her desk. He stood like a threatening dark presence over her.

'I don't need a break. I'm coping perfectly.'

'I disagree.' He laid an envelope on the desk.

Just for a moment panic swallowed her. Lisa stared at the envelope, scarcely daring to breathe. What could be inside it? A letter of dismissal?

She glanced up at him, her lips dry. 'What is it?' she demanded.

'Open it and see.' The dark eyes were shuttered. 'I

was going to leave it on your desk for you to find tomorrow morning, but it's much more satisfactory to deliver it in person.'

Lisa lifted the envelope. Her fingers were trembling. Then she held her breath and ripped it open.

The envelope did not contain a letter. The tension in her slackened and gave way to curiosity as she pulled out instead a gold-embossed card.

She read it quickly.

Then she read it again.

Perplexed, she looked up at him. 'It's an invitation.'

Vass nodded, smiling at her confusion. 'It's an invitation to you and your daughter to spend the coming weekend with me. I have a beautiful house overlooking St Ives Bay. You'll find a couple of days there most therapeutic.'

'But I can't. . .!' Lisa blinked. 'I couldn't possibly even think of it——!'

'You can and you shall.' Vass cut short her protests. He looked into her eyes. 'You have no choice. I command it.'

CHAPTER EIGHT

LISA couldn't figure out quite how she felt about this development.

Part of her, of course, was grateful. She *was* tired, and a weekend on the Cornish coast, relaxing, breathing in the clean sea air, would no doubt do her a power of good. That was if she was *capable* of relaxing, she thought doubtfully, throughout such an extended dose of Alexander Vass's company!

Over the past few weeks they'd been rubbing along fairly civilly, though not without the occasional spark flying between them. But the only reason for that relatively peaceful state of affairs was, quite simply, that Lisa had been so busy that their paths had very rarely crossed.

An entire weekend, however, in each other's company. . .! That would simply be asking for trouble! They'd probably spend the entire time at one another's throats!

Emily, by contrast, had no misgivings.

'We're going to the seaside! Oh, Mummy, we can build a sand-castle! We haven't been to the seaside for ages!'

Lisa had put aside her own doubts and hugged her little daughter. 'We'll build the biggest, most beautiful sand-castle ever,' she promised her. 'And, if it's not too cold, we can go for a paddle.'

No one could have accused her of neglecting Emily recently. She'd made a point of spending every spare minute she could with her. Every instant of her time from when she got back from work till it was time for Emily to be tucked up in bed was devoted exclusively to her precious little daughter. It was only once she was sure that Emily was asleep that she would pull out her plastic bag and get down to work.

It was the same at weekends. She would spend all day with her daughter and then work on her designs until late in the evening. But she was aware that she had been preoccupied a lot of the time, all too aware of the mountain of work before her, and that it was rather a long time since she and her daughter had had any special outings together.

So she had smiled and squashed her own reservations. 'We're going to have a wonderful time,' she had promised the smiling five-year-old. And they would, she had resolved. Emily deserved it.

It was on Thursday afternoon, as she was passing Vass's office, that Lisa struck her head round the door and reminded him, 'You'd better give me directions to your house. I don't know that corner of Cornwall too well.'

'Then you're in for a treat.' Vass glanced up and smiled at her. 'But, don't worry, you'll have no need of directions. We'll all be going down together.'

And so it was that, just after five on Friday evening, a large black Bentley, with not a sign of a dent anywhere, drew up outside Lisa's little terraced cottage and waited while she darted into Josey's to collect her daughter, then into her own house to pick up their luggage.

The little girl generously offered her approval. 'What a big, nice car!' Then, as she climbed into the back seat, she added loyally to her mother, 'But it doesn't have nice blue seats like ours does!'

Then to the accompanying curious twitch of a dozen net curtains, and a wave and smile from Josey and Charlie, they were gliding off down the narrow little street, rather like, Lisa thought, a ship gliding across water. A few minutes later they had reached the main road and were heading through a clear November evening towards the north side of the spectacular Cornish peninsula.

For better or for worse, the weekend had started.

Lisa had expected to be impressed by Vass's seaside abode. But she was more than just impressed, she was totally overwhelmed.

As she climbed out of the car she gazed, wide-eyed, around her. 'This is glorious!' she exclaimed. 'Absolute magic! I've never seen anywhere like it in my life!'

Nor had she. Seaview, a sprawling white villa that would have looked equally at home on some Greek island, was set high on a bluff overlooking the sea, poised like some magical fairy-tale castle, its silhouette sharp against the darkening autumn sky, at its feet the rocky shore that tumbled to the sea.

'I'm glad you like it.' Vass was gathering their bags from the car boot and leading Lisa and a wide-eyed Emily across a courtyard to the front door of the house.

The door opened before they reached it. A woman

stepped out, smiling. 'Mr Vass, there you are at last!'
She nodded to Lisa. 'You must be Mrs Howell. I'm
pleased to meet you.' She held out her hand. 'I'm Mrs
Birkin, the housekeeper.' Then she stooped with a
broad smile to address Emily. 'And this charming little
girl must be your daughter.'

It was not what she had been expecting. None of it,
Lisa decided. Not this breathtaking house, nor its even
more breathtaking surroundings, and certainly not the
warm, welcoming atmosphere she had been met with.

She had expected Vass's home to be as coolly
functional as his office. But it was not like that at all. It
was—dared she say it?—homely, with its well-worn
Persian rugs on the floor, its assortment of polished
antique furniture, its pictures on the walls and its velvet
curtains. It had that quality of making you feel like an
old friend who had visited there many times before.

Vass, too, seemed different in these different surroundings. In the office, like a typical Cancerian, he
seemed to have time for just one thing. Work. And
that sometimes made him seem a little remote.

But the man who sat with her now in the huge heated
conservatory that overlooked the gently foaming
waters of the bay, dotted here and there with the lights
of bobbing buoys, seemed relaxed and clearly in his
element. All the shadows had lifted from his strong
dark face.

He took a mouthful of his brandy and glanced across
at her, leaning back into the comfort of his upholstered
wicker armchair. 'I'm glad you like it here. I think
you'll find it relaxing. I know I do. For me, just being
here's a tonic.'

Lisa smiled. 'I can believe that. It has that effect. I've only been here a matter of hours, but I feel as though it's been more like a week!'

She wasn't joking. The effect had been instantaneous. Though it was only over dinner that Lisa had begun to realise just how much she needed this rest. It had been glorious just to sit there at the huge dining table, with the sounds of the sea wafting up through the open window, feeling her exhaustion slip away from her, while the energetic Mrs Birkin set before the three of them course after delicious course.

And now, with Emily tucked up in bed, she was sharing a drink with Vass before bedtime.

He took a mouthful of his cognac. 'Everyone says that. Everyone who comes here finds this place therapeutic.'

Everyone. That meant Nina. The thought pricked her instantly. She felt shame at herself, and alarm. What was getting into her?

With composure she forced a smile and sat back in her wicker armchair, raising her own glass to her lips. 'I'm sure they do.' As the brandy kicked inside her another, quite inappropriate thought occurred to her. Where was Nina this weekend? Maybe, after all, his 'dearest Nina' did not have such a singular place in his life.

The way that thought pleased her both horrified and bewildered her. She took another quick mouthful of her brandy and added quickly, 'Do you live here permanently? I mean, is this your main home, or just a weekend retreat?'

'It's my main home as much as I can make it so. I

also have a flat in Belgravia in London, and, when I'm
spending my working week at Silver Star Navigation, I
occasionally sleep there if I have a late dinner appointment. Otherwise, this is my regular base.'

Perhaps Nina stayed in London and received only
occasional visits. Lisa's mind, for some reason, like a
dog with a bone, could not let go of the subject of
Nina.

She said, feeling angry with herself, 'It's a long drive
to London. You must spend most of your time
commuting?'

Vass shook his head. 'That used to be the case, but
these days I'm a little better organised. I have a private
helicopter to take me to and fro.'

'I might have known!' There was an edge to the
exclamation. And Lisa hated herself for that. It made
her sound envious, when what had really caused it was
her own anger at herself.

He had caught that hard edge. His eyes narrowed as
he looked at her. 'Maybe, one day, you too will have
your own helicopter. When you finally become a world-
famous designer.'

'How generous of you to say so.' She knew he did
not mean it. He was simply laughing at her in that
condescending way he had. 'But, really,' she assured
him, 'you don't have to humour me.'

'Humour you? Why should I humour you?'

'I have no idea. Perhaps you feel it's part of your
duty as my host.'

To her annoyance, Vass smiled and held her eyes a
moment. Then he glanced down into his glass. 'Why,

don't you believe it? Don't you believe you'll be a world-class designer one day?'

As a matter of fact, she did. She had certainly dreamed it. But she was not about to reveal such precious dreams to him.

Looking back at him, she said, 'The only ambition I have at the moment is to survive my eighteen months with G.W. Fashions. Anything after that will be a bonus.'

Vass laughed. 'Has it really been so bad? I'd rather got the impression that you were coming round to quite enjoying working for me.'

It was true, of course, but, wondering why, she denied it. 'How on earth could I possibly enjoy working for someone who crushes my creative instincts in the way that you do?'

'Do I? I don't think so. All I've done is guide you.'

'Guide me? Is that what you call it? I'd call it a little more than guidance!' Even as she said it, Lisa was asking herself where on earth this display of indignation was coming from. She had long ago stopped resenting their original professional clashes, and these days their disagreements tended to be over minor details, with her ending up the victor as often as he did.

'You're far too sensitive—as I keep telling you.' Vass looked back at her through narrowed dark eyes. 'I've never tried to crush your creative instincts. But you need a little guidance. You need a firm hand.'

'Like a horse, you mean? A firm hand on the reins? To make sure I jump whenever you tell me?'

Vass laughed at that. 'I see you more as a sailboat, skimming freely across the ocean, responding naturally

to the winds and the currents—but with a light hand
on the tiller now and then to make sure you make the
most of your capabilities.'

It was an oddly pleasing picture. Lisa almost smiled
at him. But then he added, 'You definitely need a hand
on the tiller. You are at times an exceptionally fiery-
headed young woman.'

Fire and water. The two unmixable elements. She
was fiery by temperament, Lisa had always known that,
and he, a Cancerian to his fingertips, was all shifting,
unfathomable water.

She did not argue with him. She simply put to him,
'You disapprove of that, don't you? What you call my
fiery-headedness?'

'Disapprove?' Vass shook his head. 'Not in the
slightest. In fact, I find it really quite appealing.'

He held her eyes as he said it, making her heart skid
inside her, the touch of his gaze suddenly so soft, so
caressing, that it suffused her entire body with a glow
of sensuous pleasure.

With an effort Lisa forced herself to swallow back
the feeling and kept her voice devoid of emotion as she
countered, 'If it's so appealing then why do you feel
the need to suppress it?'

'Not suppress. That's the wrong word. But at times
it needs harnessing.' He smiled. 'Occasionally it needs
to be given direction. Fire is light, fire is energy. But,
uncontrolled, it can be, at best, unproductive, and at
worst it can be downright destructive.'

'Like the fire that burned your store-room.'

'Yes, that was destructive.' His eyes were flat as he

said it. It was impossible to know whether he still believed she'd been responsible for that.

Lisa looked back at him steadily. 'I didn't start that fire. My kind of fire is not the destructive kind. I really do wish you would believe that.'

He answered her with a look that told her nothing. Then he took a sip of his brandy and put to her, dark eyes watching her, 'In the end you were happy, were you not, with the designs we finally decided to go ahead with?'

'What choice did I have?' She, too, could be elusive, though she could not quite disguise the smile in her eyes as she said it. For the truth was she had, in fact, been deeply satisfied with that second, much sweated over batch of sketches. They were better than the originals. Much, much better. And not just in the context of G.W. Fashions and their suitability for a mass market, but in a simple design sense. They were purer, subtler.

She looked up into his eyes. 'OK, I'll be honest. In the end, I was grateful for your "guidance".'

'Guidance was all it was. The designs are all yours. And I'd be sad if I thought you were less than happy with them.'

Lisa looked back at him, oddly rankled by that assertion. Alexander Vass, sad because she might not be happy? After all, he was the man who'd sacked her predecessor simply in order to make room for her. This sudden declaration of sensitivity struck her as out of character and oddly demeaning. He had plenty of faults, but she had not believed falseness to be among them.

He surveyed her silent face, then suddenly he asked, changing the subject unexpectedly, in that way he sometimes did, 'So, how do your family feel about you working for me?'

'You mean my parents?'

He nodded. 'Your parents. . .and anyone else in your family who takes an interest in what you're up to.'

'I have no other family besides my parents.' She said it sharply, as though to cut him down. That unexpected insincerity had annoyed her. Far more, probably, than it ought to have done.

'Do they live in Liskeard?' He remained unruffled. It would take more than a sharp tongue to cut down Alexander Vass.

'They live outside Darlington.'

'So far away?'

'It's not really so far. Only a few hours by train.'

'Do you visit them often?'

'Whenever I can.' When I can afford to, she really meant. And that was not as often as she might have wished.

'So, what brought you down here?' He drained his cognac. 'This is an unlikely place, I would have thought, for a girl from Darlington to end up.'

'No more unlikely, surely, for a girl from Darlington than it is for a boy from the East End of London?'

Vass laughed. 'I suppose you're right. I hadn't thought of it like that. You see, strange as it may seem, I always felt I belonged here. My first visit to Cornwall was on a school trip. I was about twelve years old, and I fell in love with the place instantly. I decided then that, as soon as I could afford it, I'd build myself a house here by the sea. And that's exactly what I did.'

At the light in his eyes, Lisa forgot her annoyance. She smiled. 'I would say that you very much belong here. You seem to have an affinity with the place.'

'Do I?'

She nodded. 'Very definitely. I've felt that from the very first moment we got here.'

It was that Cancerian spirit of his, of course. She knew that. Cancer, the crab, and water belonged together.

As he held her eyes for a moment a look passed between them, deeply compassionate, oddly intimate. As though he knew she had understood this essential part of him, and approved, even welcomed, that understanding.

'And you?' he asked her. 'Do you feel that you belong here?'

'You mean here in Cornwall?' He could not possibly mean here in the bay, yet her heart had jumped in confusion for a moment. She glanced away quickly and stared down into her cognac, fighting the sudden strange charge of emotion that shot through her. 'Yes, these days I think of Cornwall as my home. I can't imagine living anywhere else.'

'But you still haven't told me what brought you here in the first place.' She could feel his eyes on her, warming her skin.

She glanced up. 'I came here because I married a Cornishman. My husband, Tony; he was from here.'

'Ah, I see.'

'We met in Darlington. He was on holiday. Less

than a year later we got married and I moved down here and eventually found myself a job. In the same place as Tony. He was a trainee manager with the company.'

'I see.' Vass was very still now, the dark eyes watching her. 'But you could have gone back north. I mean after you were left alone.'

'After Tony died?' She had no trouble saying it. Tony's tragic death, that terrible ending of his young life, was something she had long ago come to terms with. Yet there was a stiff note in her voice. She knew what Vass was thinking—that she was still in a state of secret mourning for her dead husband.

She was unsure now why she had decided to let him go on believing that, and she felt torn by a sudden desire to tell him the truth. But why? she wondered. Why does it matter? She looked down into her drink and answered evasively, 'I suppose I could have gone back to Darlington, but I preferred to stay down here.'

As she had expected, Vass's response was diplomatic. He smiled. 'Well, let me tell you, there's nothing in the world that could ever tear me away from this place.' He raised one dark eyebrow. 'More cognac?' he suggested.

Lisa shook her head. 'No, thank you. I think it's bedtime.' She drained her glass and laid it on the cane table. 'No doubt Emily will be up at the crack of dawn, all geared up and ready to go. I'd better make sure I've got enough energy to keep up with her.'

As she started to stand up Lisa was aware that she had not intended this abrupt departure. It was early yet, just after ten o'clock, and, in spite of the way he ruffled her sometimes, she'd been quite enjoying their quiet little chat.

After all, these inevitable little skirmishes were part and parcel of their relationship. They no longer upset her. In a way, she even enjoyed them. They were like set pieces in their ongoing battle that these days was devoid of any real malice.

But something had happened when she'd touched on the subject of Tony. She hovered awkwardly for a moment, wishing she could dispel the cloud of misunderstanding that suddenly seemed to hang between them. But why should it matter? she asked herself again. Why am I bothering even to think of such things?

He had remained seated as she stood there, hovering uncertainly, but now, with a shuttered smile, he rose to his feet. 'I'll bid you goodnight. You know your way to your room? If there's anything you need, just let Mrs Birkin know.'

'Oh, I'm sure there's nothing. And yes, I know my way.' Still she hovered. 'You're not turning in yet?'

'No, I think I'll go for a short walk along the seafront. It's still a little early for me.'

'Good idea.' She nodded awkwardly. 'OK. Goodnight, then. I'll see you in the morning.'

'Bright and early.' He continued to stand there, watching as she made her way across the conservatory, then through the high arched doorway that led into the sitting-room.

And she just knew that, if she had not brought up the subject of Tony, he would have invited her to join him in his walk along the shore. And she wondered, as she headed for the hallway and the staircase that led up to her bedroom on the first floor, why the fact that that had not happened troubled her so.

But it did. Long after she had climbed into bed she continued to be haunted by the oddly regretful image of herself and Alexander strolling together, arm in arm, along the moonlit shore.

And there was another thought, too, that would not let her go. As he walked beneath the moonlight, was he thinking of Nina?

CHAPTER NINE

LISA slept like a stone in the big double bed—far comfier than her own bed at home—and awoke to find Emily already up and dressed, pulling on her green rubber wellies.

'Alexander said I ought to wear these,' she explained, bright-cheeked, as Lisa sat up with a start. 'I had on my trainers, but he said they'd get wet. We're going down to the beach to look for mussels.'

Lisa glanced at her watch on the bedside table. Good grief, it was almost twenty-past ten! 'Have you had breakfast, young lady?' she demanded, jumping from the bed, feeling guilty. 'You can't go out there without eating first.'

Emily grinned. 'Don't worry, I had breakfast ages ago. Me and Alexander. We had crossings and honey.'

'*Crossings* and honey?' Lisa smiled as she bent to kiss her. 'I think you mean *croissants* and honey, sweetheart.' She straightened the child's anorak, and frowned a small frown. 'And who told you to call him Alexander, I'd like to know? I thought I told you to call him Mr Vass?'

'He told me. He said he'd be cross if I didn't. He said he was cross with you because you keep calling him Mr Vass.'

'Did he, by golly?' Lisa pulled a face. 'And where

133

did you say he was taking you now? Down to the seashore to look for mussels?'

Emily nodded. 'If we find enough we're going to have them for dinner tonight.'

'OK, then.' Lisa kissed her and released her. 'But just make sure that you're a good girl. Just do exactly what Mr—er—Alexander. . .tells you.'

'I will. See you later, Mummy.' Emily headed for the door. Then, on excited little legs, she was hurrying downstairs.

Lisa stood in the bedroom doorway and watched her go. Alexander, indeed! she thought with a wry smile. Well, to her he would always remain Mr Vass, whether it made him cross or not!

She showered and dressed quickly in tan cords and a cream woollen top, brushing her hair into a cascade of soft curls. She felt great, better rested than she'd felt for weeks now, the little aches of fatigue she'd been growing used to now all miraculously ironed out.

There was only one small regret she had about her tardiness: she was clearly far too late for breakfast, and she was feeling absolutely ravenous!

Perhaps, she wondered as she hurried downstairs, if she could find the kitchen she might be able to make a cup of coffee and a slice of toast for herself. No doubt she had missed out on the 'crossings'!

She was halfway down the corridor that led to the back of the house when, out of nowhere, Mrs Birkin appeared.

'There you are, Mrs Howell! I hope you slept well?' the housekeeper smiled her usual cheery smile. 'If you'd like to go through to the conservatory, I'll bring you breakfast in just a minute.'

'But, Mrs Birkin, I couldn't possibly expect you to go to all the trouble——'

'It's no trouble at all.' The good woman was adamant. 'The breakfast table is set and waiting for you. Would you like me to make you some eggs and bacon?'

'No, thanks. Just coffee. That's terribly good of you. And a couple of croissants, if there are any.'

'Of course there are.' She winked at Lisa. 'In this house we're very easygoing. We don't have strict timetables for meals. So just you relax and I'll be with you in a couple of minutes.'

Lisa smiled to herself as she walked back along the corridor that led to the drawing-room and the conservatory. It was a smile of reflective curiosity.

Easygoing—that was the word Mrs Birkin had used, and that was precisely how she herself would describe the feel of this house. Precisely the opposite of all she'd expected! But she had ceased to be surprised, or even confused, by the constantly changing facets of Alexander Vass. In a way she was almost learning to feel quite at home with them, though there was still a sense of wariness she would probably never conquer.

And would be most unwise to try to conquer! She might have begun to feel increasingly comfortable in his company, but she knew, nevertheless, she'd be a fool to trust him. Nigel, her predecessor, had probably trusted him. And just look at what had happened to him!

It was as she was passing through the drawing-room that she paused for a moment to glance round admiringly at the décor. Yesterday she hadn't had a chance to look properly. She'd simply had an impression of a stunningly beautiful room without having time to admire its contents.

And there was plenty to admire, she realised at once as her gaze travelled over the Regency bureau, the Chippendale cabinet, the Aubusson rug. It was a glorious room. The whole house was glorious. Even the *en suite* bathroom of the bedroom she shared with Emily could be described by no other word than glorious!

She stepped forward a moment to admire a cabinet of gleaming silver—quite the most beautiful collection imaginable—and it was in that moment that something caught her eye. A silver-framed photograph on one of the little side-tables. As she gazed down at it her heart missed a beat.

It was a photograph of Vass, a very recent one, she judged, and in it he was smiling that magical, luminous smile of his that never failed to catch at Lisa's heart-strings. And, as he smiled, he was gazing into the eyes of an extraordinarily beautiful dark-haired girl.

For a moment Lisa could not tear her eyes away. The girl was Nina. Instantly she knew that. His 'dearest Nina'. Her heart turned over.

Another thought came to her, out of nowhere. A memory of that facetious remark Vass had once made about opposites and their power to attract.

So much for that theory! With her dark hair and eyes and the subtle air of mystery that shone from her features, Nina was far from being his opposite. More like some female mirror image!

Abruptly Lisa stepped away, quelling the strange pang inside her. It was none of her business and it mattered to her not one iota. On brisk steps she headed through the door to the conservatory.

She had successfully banished the photograph from her mind and was gazing outside, down at the sunlit seashore, her eyes searching for Emily, when Mrs Birkin appeared.

'Here we are!' The woman laid before her a pot of coffee, a jug of orange juice and a dish of piping hot rolls and croissants.

'That looks delicious! Thank you, Mrs Birkin.'

'Just give me a shout if you want any more.'

Lisa dived in hungrily, spreading butter and honey on a croissant, and reflecting as she washed down the first bite with coffee that it was even more delicious than it looked.

It was midway through her third croissant that Lisa caught sight of little Emily, striding, hand in hand with Vass, along the path that led up from the shore to the house. And there was something about the easy way they were together, evidently in the full flow of conversation, that sent a quick uneasy dart of emotion rushing through her.

Dear, sweet Emily. The picture she presented was the echo of a picture that Lisa, long ago, before she had put all such thoughts behind her, had so often regretfully imagined. The child walking hand in hand with her father.

But, even as the thought occurred to her, she squashed it angrily. Alexander Vass was not the kind of man whom she was likely to involve in such a fantasy. One could scarcely describe him as some kind of father-figure! And he was certainly not the kind of man she would want as a father for her daughter!

She was pouring herself more coffee when he walked into the conservatory. Lisa glanced past him. 'Where's Emily?' she demanded.

'In the kitchen with Mrs Birkin.' He sat down in the chair opposite her. 'She insisted on helping her clean the mussels.'

'Did you find many?' She glanced away as she said it and concentrated on stirring her coffee. For some reason she felt thrown by his sudden lone appearance, by his informal friendly manner, by the smile in his eyes.

He was dressed in a pair of well-worn-looking jeans that were stuffed into the tops of his black rubber boots, with a thick roll-neck sweater, a dark navy blue, beneath the battered-looking dark green waterproof jacket. And there was a vigour about him, a brightness of eye, an easiness about the way he held himself, that almost seemed to threaten her in some indefinable way. Lisa wished he hadn't sat down beside her.

'We found a few,' he told her, answering her question about the mussels, pulling off his jacket as he did so and draping it carelessly over the back of the chair. 'But I'm afraid Mrs Birkin is going to have to raid the freezer if we're to have enough for three tonight.'

'You don't have to do that. There's really no need.'

'Oh, but there is.' He reached for a cup and poured himself coffee. 'I promised Emily mussels tonight, and mussels are what she's going to have.'

For some reason that irked her. 'How very conscientious. Are you always so conscientious about keeping promises?'

'I try to be.' He looked at her. 'And are you,' he put to her, 'always so possessive about your daughter?'

'Possessive?' Lisa blinked at him. 'I'm not possessive in the slightest!' She knew that to be true, though Emily meant the world to her. And yet she *had* felt something, some quick negative flicker at his casual reference to the promise he had made Emily, just as she had felt that uneasy dart inside her when she had caught sight of them earlier, coming up the path together.

These reactions were neither jealousy nor possessiveness, she was absolutely certain of that. But what they were she could not quite put her finger on.

Vass was watching her as he stirred sugar into his coffee. 'So why do you disapprove of my getting along so well with Emily?'

'I don't disapprove. I can assure you, I'm delighted. There's nothing I want more than that my daughter should grow up to be the sort of person who gets along with everybody.'

'Even people like me?' He smiled as he said it. But it was a quagmire question, best left unanswered.

So Lisa did not answer it. Instead she turned it round on him. 'And what kind of person are you, Mr Vass?'

'Difficult to fathom, so I'm told.' He took a mouthful of his coffee. 'You look surprised.'

'I am.'

'You don't agree that I'm hard to fathom?'

'Oh, I agree with that.' She smiled a wry smile.

'What surprises me is that you're aware of it. I hadn't believed you capable of such self-knowledge.'

That was a little more forthright than she had intended, but he simply smiled a smile of dry amusement. 'I'll tell you something else that may surprise you. I'm difficult to fathom, but I'm well worth the effort.'

'Now that *does* surprise me.'

'Yes, I thought it would. But, take my word for it, beneath this slightly tough façade I'm a quite exceptionally charming fellow. So those who know me intimately insist.'

Lisa instantly found herself thinking of Nina. Nina, she had no doubt, would possess such intimate knowledge.

She pushed the thought from her, annoyed at herself. What did she care about such details of his life?

Yet she found herself observing with an edge of sarcasm, 'Indeed? Is that what your lady-friends tell you?'

'Quite unanimously.'

'Perhaps they're being polite. Women have this weakness. We don't like hurting people's feelings, and we know how fragile the male ego is.'

'You're so right.' Unperturbed, he smiled across at her. Then he continued to watch her as he poured himself more coffee. He leaned back in his chair. 'So tell me, Lisa. What do your men-friends tell you, about you?'

'What men-friends are you talking about?'

He took a sip of his coffee. 'Ah, yes, of course. You've already told me, you don't have any.' He paused an instant. A shadow touched his features. 'So, if you did have some, what do you think they'd tell you?' Suddenly some of the lightness had vanished from his tone.

'I have no idea.'

'Don't you? *I* think I do.'

'Really?' All at once she felt oddly threatened. Like a mouse sensing a cat about to pounce. But she could not resist asking, walking straight into his waiting jaws, 'So, since you know so much, what do you think they'd tell me?'

Vass did not hesitate. 'That you're wasting your life. That it's time you stopped living in the past and started moving into the present.'

She had known he'd say that, and it confirmed her suspicions. He really did believe she was still mourning Tony. But before she could decide whether or not finally to deny it he stopped her in her tracks with another accusation—one that she had definitely not seen coming.

'You should stop fighting so hard to keep people at a distance. You seem absolutely terrified of letting anyone near you.'

Lisa blinked. 'What are you talking about? Who, for instance?'

'Me, for instance. Do you deny it? You're absolutely desperate to keep me at arm's length.'

Lisa felt the colour ebb and flow in her face. She did not like the sound of those words he was using. Desperate. Terrified. They sounded oddly undermining. She smiled at him uneasily. 'I wouldn't call myself desperate.'

'And what would you call yourself?'

'I really don't know.' Suddenly she felt confused, uncertain of what she was being accused of and equally uncertain of how to defend herself. If it was true what he said, that she kept him at arm's length, surely there could only be one reason for that? And the reason was, quite simply, that she did not like him.

But she could scarcely tell him that. As he continued to watch her she delved in her brain and came up with a substitute. 'I think you're misinterpreting the situation, Mr Vass. I tend to be a little formal because you're my boss.'

A smile touched his eyes. Vass shook his head. '"Mr Vass." That just about sums it up. Do you really expect me to believe that it's out of respect for my position that you insist on calling me Mr Vass?'

'Of course it is.'

'Rubbish!'

'It isn't rubbish!'

'Even your daughter calls me Alexander.'

'That's because you told her to.'

'I told you the same thing.' The black eyes narrowed. 'More than once, as I recall.'

'I know you did.' Lisa's heart was pumping. This conversation was making her feel uncomfortable and vulnerable. She dropped her hands to her lap. 'Maybe I'm old-fashioned, but I prefer to keep things formal. I just wouldn't feel comfortable calling you. . .less formally.'

Vas shook his head and smiled at her awkwardness. 'Alexander's the name. Try using it a couple of times.' He spoke softly, but there was no denying the impatience in his voice. 'I promise you, you'll soon get the hang of it.'

There was a silence. Lisa stared down at the table-cloth, wishing she could think of some excuse to go. She was aware that the pumping of her heart was almost deafening and that the hands in her lap were clenched unnaturally tight.

She felt chastised, like a child, confused and fool-ish—and appalled at how deeply his displeasure had affected her. It was just like last night again, when the mood had changed between them and she had left to go to bed, filled with regrets. That he could affect her this way was deeply shocking.

But the moment was saved as, with a clatter of small feet, Emily came bursting into the conservatory.

'Mummy, we're having mussels for dinner tonight! We caught them, me and Alexander! And Mrs Birkin say she's going to cook them with garlic!'

'Sounds delicious.' Lisa caught her and hugged her gratefully. She kissed the child's head. 'Are you enjoy-ing yourself?'

As Emily nodded enthusiastically and kissed her mother's cheek Alexander glanced quickly at his watch. 'How about a drive before lunchtime?' he suggested. 'I'll show the two of you round the area, then we can stop off for lunch wherever takes our fancy.'

He winked across at Emily. 'Only a light lunch, of course. We have to leave room for those mussels tonight!'

And that was exactly what they did. They had lunch at a hotel overlooking the sea after a leisurely meander in the big black Bentley round the magnificent, twisting coastline road.

For Lisa the experience was a revelation—and a chance to shake off her earlier strange feelings. As far as Vass was concerned, that episode at breakfast seemed to have been totally forgotten, and, with her little daughter around to distract her, Lisa soon managed to chase it from her mind.

And, besides, the trip itself was sheer pleasure.

'I had no idea it was so beautiful around here,' Lisa murmured as they paused for a moment on a promontory to admire the view that stretched out before them. The craggy, rocky shore, the curling, frothing tide, the deep blue waters that seemed to stretch forever. 'I can scarcely believe I've lived in Cornwall for all these years and haven't seen any of this before!'

'I expect you've been too busy.' Alexander caught her eye. 'Earning a living, bringing up your child.'

Lisa flushed and looked away. If she hadn't known for a fact that he liked nothing about her she might have mistaken that note in his voice for admiration.

She said, staring out to sea, struggling with strange emotions, 'In future I'll make time. For Emily's sake. She deserves to grow up enjoying all of this.'

And that was when he almost caused her to drop with astonishment off the promontory.

'Feel free,' he told her, 'to spend your weekends at Seaview, even when I'm not here, any time you like.'

Was he joking? Was she hearing things? Lisa spun round to look at him. 'Oh, I couldn't possibly!' she protested.

The dark gaze looked back at her, hard to decipher,

though at least she could see he did not appear to be joking. 'Think about it, anyway.' He smiled a quick smile. 'Consider the offer to be part of our agreement.'

Lisa smiled back stiffly. 'Thank you. I'll think about it.' But in her heart she knew there was no way in the world she would ever take up this incredible offer, which had been prompted by motives she could not even begin to fathom. As it was, this weekend had probably been a mistake.

As though to belie that negative conclusion, the day proceeded to prove both relaxing and enjoyable. When all three of them were together they got on remarkably well.

In the afternoon they went to Land's End and Vass helped Emily pick pebbles from the beath. Then they built a sand-castle with ramparts and a moat and turrets, and stopped off at a café on their way home and treated themselves to a delicious cream tea.

It was there that they bumped into some friends of Alexander's, a couple with two young children of their own, and spent an hour chatting with them round the café table.

They were an ordinary family, all born and bred locally, but their relationship with Alexander was both friendly and relaxed. Lisa found herself watching him as they chatted about this and that, quietly amazed at the easy way he fitted in with them. She kept trying to tell herself that he could no longer surprise her, and yet he continued to do just that.

She'd been introduced to the others initially as a friend. It was only as the conversation progressed that her function at G.W. Fashions was revealed.

'I wish I had such a talent,' Karen, the young wife, enthused to her. 'I would love to be able to do something creative like that.'

Alexander smiled and, almost proprietorially, laid a hand along the back of Lisa's chair. 'Not many of us are blessed with a talent like Lisa's. I was damned lucky to find her, to bump into her the way I did.'

As he said that last part about 'bumping into her' he glanced across at Lisa, and a flicker passed between them as, silently, they shared their private joke. And Lisa was aware of a tightening in her stomach. That fleeting, spontaneous intimacy had stirred something within her.

Later, Alexander called the waitress and ordered another round of scones.

'What about the mussels? We'll have no room left for them!' Emily protested unconvincingly as the scones were duly brought.

'Don't worry,' Alexander promised, 'we'll have plenty of room for the mussels. Before dinner we'll all go for a brisk walk along the beach and make sure we work up a nice big appetite.'

Needless to say, his prediction was right, and Mrs Birkin's garlic mussels, along with three generous portions of roast chicken and a delicious apple pie, were hungrily consumed. Sleepy and satisfied, Emily was only too willing to be tucked up in bed, just after nine o'clock.

'She's had a wonderful day. I can't thank you enough.' Lisa came back downstairs again after bidding her goodnight to find Alexander in the drawing-room, pouring them each a brandy. While she'd been gone he'd put some music on the stereo. A gentle Mozart sonata drifted round the room.

He smiled. 'I hope you had a wonderful day as well? I know I did. I haven't enjoyed myself so much for a long time.'

'Nor me.' She said it spontaneously, without thinking. And it surprised her a little that it was true.

A mere lull, she told herself, smiling, in an ongoing battle.

He was watching her. 'Shall we go through to the conservatory? It's nice to watch the sea at night.'

Lisa nodded. 'OK.' And, as he finished pouring their brandies, she walked ahead of him through the open doorway and stood for a moment before the huge window, listening to the music, gazing out to sea, aware of a sense of peace and deep contentment. She sighed. It had been a long time since she had felt this way.

She jumped as he touched her arm. She had not heard him approach her. And now he was standing at her elbow, holding out her glass.

Sudden confusion overtook her. She wanted to move away. But she could not move away without appearing gauche and childish. So, instead, she said, 'I really want to thank you for being so good with Emily today.'

Even as she said it, she recognised what she was doing—attempting to put some distance between them by drawing in her daughter, as a shield. Alexander had been right. She did it all the time. And what was worrying was that the ploy had not been triggered by dislike.

Alexander simply smiled. His dark eyes were twinkling. 'You're not feeling possessive any more, I see. You don't mind my being friends with Emily?'

'I was never possessive.' Instantly she defended herself, just as she had when he had made that accusation before. But, even as she spoke, her heart jumped inside her. And in that instant she understood two things.

The first thing she understood was the plain and simple reason for those negative feelings she had originally experienced on seeing how well her daughter and Alexander got on together. And the second thing she understood was the reason why she was indeed so desperate to keep him at a distance.

But she had no chance to reflect on this double revelation. For, before another thought could form in her head, he was laying aside their brandy glasses and gently reaching out for her, one arm sliding round her waist. Then he was bending towards her, very softly, to kiss her.

CHAPTER TEN

SIMULTANEOUSLY Lisa felt her heart stop dead and a rush of excitement unleash within her. Vass's arms embraced her, lightly yet firmly, pinning her slender body against his, and his lips all at once were pressing down on her lips, drawing the life from her, setting her on fire.

One part of her could not believe it was happening, and perhaps that was why she did not resist. In a moment she would open her eyes to discover that it had all been an incredible, fantastical dream.

Yet she knew it was no dream. No dream could have awakened the flood of sensations and swirling emotions, like a dam-burst, that had suddenly exploded within her, flowing too swiftly, too eagerly, to control.

She felt her hands slide to his shoulders as his grip around her tightened, and the hardness of those shoulders, the power she could feel in them, sent a shiver of long-forgotten yearning tearing through her.

With a sigh her lips parted, welcoming him, tasting him, and all at once her mind and her body had grown tight with a sudden aching, urgent need.

'Lisa, sweet Lisa.' He had leaned back a little, brushing her hair back softly with his fingers, pausing to gaze long and deep into her eyes.

She looked back at him. 'Alexander,' she whispered.

Suddenly, there it was, his name on her lips!

He smiled. 'There, that didn't hurt so much, after all, did it?' As she smiled back at him, shaking her head in agreement, he let his fingers trail softly through her silken hair, then slide round to cup her chin and tilt it gently. 'I would have kissed you long ago if I'd known a simple kiss could have so miraculous an effect.'

As he kissed her again, softly, her muscles tensed in expectation, waiting for his lips to consume her once more. But, instead, he drew back and reached for her brandy glass. He handed it to her, smiling. 'Here,' he said. 'This is yours.'

Then he was reaching for his own glass and inviting her to sit in one of the wicker armchairs overlooking the bay while he seated himself in the chair beside her.

Lisa looked across at him. Her heart was still racing. Why had he stopped? she found herself wondering. Had he sensed the reckless hunger in her? Had he been afraid that things might go too far?

Or had he simply decided to spin things out a little? Certainly, as he leaned back in his chair and looked across at her, there was no sign of coolness in the dark eyes. The thought sent a shiver of excitement through her that instantly she sought to crush. Was she actually planning to aid and abet him in this unexpected, meaningless sexual dalliance? No, she chastised herself. She most definitely was not!

Yet, all the same, as he took a mouthful of his brandy and reached across with his free hand to take hold of hers Lisa made no effort to extricate her fingers. Holding hands is harmless, she told herself.

He was looking across at her. 'I'm surprised that you

have never remarried. Six years alone is rather a long time.'

'Meaning?' Had he intended that remark to be offensive? After all, what he seemed to be suggesting was that a woman with her not inconsiderable sex drive might have been expected, long ago, to have found a man to satisfy it.

As her fingers tensed in his he stroked them lightly. 'Meaning,' he smiled, 'that you are a beautiful and sensuous young woman. Such a woman was not meant to be alone.'

Lisa felt herself relax. No offence had been intended. If anything, she sensed, rather the opposite. She smiled and looked back at him. 'When you have a child to consider you don't go rushing into the first relationship that comes along. You have to consider things very carefully, and quite often you end up making decisions that you might not have made if you'd been alone.'

'So, there have been other suitors?'

Lisa nodded. 'Naturally.'

'But none you were tempted to set up home with. None who got close enough to lure you into marriage?'

Lisa shook her head. 'No, I'm afraid not.' Then she threw him a shrewd look. 'But please don't believe that I'm pining away for the lack of a man in my life. Emily and I manage very well.'

He was still holding her hand, his fingers moving against hers, the action an odd mix of soothing and exciting. Her heartbeat flared and subsided in a disjointed kind of rhythm.

'Yes, I remember you saying that.' He paused a moment, allowing a gentle silence to flow between them. Then he continued, 'I also remember you saying that you believed you would probably never marry again.' Momentarily his fingers stilled against hers. 'Will no man ever be able to take the place of Tony?'

'That wasn't what I meant.'

'Then what was it that you did mean?'

'All I meant was that I find it hard to imagine myself setting up home with someone else again.'

'Isn't that the same thing?'

'No, it isn't.' Something clenched inside her as she said it. She was remembering the revelation that had come to her just a few short moments ago, in what seemed like another age now, before Alexander had kissed her.

'In what way is it different?' His fingers had tightened a little. 'I don't understand. Please explain.'

Lisa took a deep breath. 'There's a very big difference. To say that no man could ever take the place of Tony is to say that I've never got over his death.' She looked straight at Alexander. 'I know that's what you've been thinking. You more or less accused me of it at breakfast this morning. But I can assure you it's a long way from the truth.'

'Oh?' His fingers urged her to continue.

'I loved Tony and there was a time when I thought I'd never get over him. But I did get over him. Slowly. Gradually.' She smiled a small smile. 'I stopped mourning a long time ago.'

He looked into her eyes and, very slowly, raised her fingers to his lips. 'I'm glad to hear it. It would not be healthy still to be mourning after so many years.'

She felt the warmth of that kiss steal slowly up her

arm and wrap itself around her heart. And as she looked into his eyes, again she remembered the revelation that had so taken her by surprise.

She forced it from her mind. Frankly, it terrified her. 'Besides, as I told you,' she elaborated a little stiffly, 'in such matters I have to think of Emily.'

Their hands lay laced together on the chair arm, but Lisa did not look at him as he put to her, 'Of course you have to think of Emily, but surely there must be a couple of men out there who are capable of being a good father to your daughter?'

'Of course there are. I've even met some.' She darted him a quick smile. 'But all the men I've met who I've felt would make good fathers have invariably turned out to be men I couldn't love. . .'

'And the men you've felt you could love,' he finished for her, 'have failed to qualify as good father material?'

'Something like that.' Lisa nodded in agreement, though that assessment, she realised, was not strictly accurate. She had met no one she had even come close to loving.

That was, until now.

Emotion flooded through her.

That was, until she'd met Alexander.

As she gazed at the floor, unable to look at him, there flashed across her mind that image of two figures walking together along the path from the beach. One her daughter, the other Alexander. And again she recognised what she'd known then instantly: that she loved him and that he would make a perfect father for her daughter.

Yet the very idea was gross and implausible. No

wonder she'd struggled so hard against it, doing all in her power to keep him at a distance. To fall in love with Alexander would be a catastrophe!

And yet here she was, sitting with him in the conservatory, her hand held in his, blushing beneath his gaze.

She felt her fingers stiffen. She forced herself to look at him. 'Why are you so interested? What does it matter to you if I never remarry or find a new father for Emily?'

'I think it would be a pity. A child needs a father. And it would be nice if you were to provide her with a little brother or sister.'

Lisa had thought that herself. After all, Emily was nearly six now. But, she told herself quickly, it was really none of Alexander's business.

As though deliberately to alienate him, she tossed him a bold look. 'If I wanted, I could easily provide a sibling for Emily without all the bother of getting married.'

'And do you want that?' She had expected his disapproval, but there was only amusement in his eyes as he smiled, meeting her directness with what sounded like an invitation. 'Are you interested in recruiting the services of a man merely for the purpose of impregnation?'

'Of course not!'

Yet, even as she shot the denial at him, Lisa was aware of an unexpected reaction within her. A flare of sexual longing that was totally shameful. Her stomach twisted as in that moment she seemed to feel him pierce her loins in the act of impregnation.

Yet, though her reaction was shocking, in a way it was also reassuring. It brought her feelings for Alexander sharply into focus. She desired him, she found him physically attractive to a degree that still had the power to surprise her. But that's all there was to it. Her heart was not involved. What she'd feared might be love was something rather different. The simple animal tug of lust.

That made her feel better. She allowed her fingers to relax as his continued to twine with hers. Lust she could handle. Lust she could conquer. Lust was far less dangerous than love.

Fluidly, unhurriedly, she disentwined her fingers and curled them instead around her brandy glass. She took a slow mouthful. 'I've already told you, I have no plans, and no desire, to change my situation. Emily and I are happy as we are.' She paused and regarded him over the top of her glass. 'But what about you? Why aren't you married? Why don't you have a brood of your own?'

She had half expected that he would deflect the question. After all, though he had no compunction about digging into her private affairs, like a typical Cancerian, he was invariably reserved about his own.

But instead he told her, 'You're right, I ought to be. I ought to be married with half a dozen kids of my own. It's always been my intention, but somehow it's never happened. I guess the right girl has just never come along.'

Lisa looked back at him. 'I'm surprised to hear that.' Her heart was thumping. She was thinking of Nina. 'Surely a man like you has someone special in his life?'

Alexander shook his head. 'I'm afraid not,' he told her. 'Girlfriends, yes. But no one special.'

'No one?' Lisa continued to look into his face. 'I really do find that hard to believe.'

'Hard to believe? Why?'

'Oh, I don't know. . .' Dared she mention Nina? The card on his desk? The framed photograph of them together?

She decided against it. 'Oh, it was just a feeling. But if there isn't, there isn't. After all, you ought to know.'

Of course, she knew he was lying. But she found his lie reassuring. She clutched at it. It reminded her of the type of man he was.

The type of man it would be madness to trust.

The type of man it would be disastrous to love.

Yet she could not deny that her heart tilted inside her as he reached for her hand once more and assured her, 'I'm as free as you are. As free as a bird.' As he said it he raised her hand to his lips and grazed her flesh with the warmth of his kiss.

A yearning pierced through her, burning, like hot metal. And, folly though it was, just for a moment, more than anything in the world, Lisa wanted to believe him.

She watched him as he reached for his brandy glass and drained it, her eyes fixed on his dark profile, drinking him in. Then her breath caught as he turned, unexpectedly, to look at her, inviting her with one of his soft, easy smiles, 'I think it's time for my walk along the beach before bedtime. Perhaps this evening you'd care to join me?'

Something shifted inside her. 'Yes, that would be

nice.' She had wanted to say no, but the gesture was beyond her.

'Finish your brandy first.' He glanced at her glass, then started, unhurriedly, to rise to his feet. 'Or leave it till later, if you like.'

'I'll finish it now. There's only a drop.' She raised the glass to her lips and knocked the brandy back quickly, feeling it kick at the back of her mouth. She felt strangely at odds with herself, confused by her own emotions. She ought not to be going, but she could not help herself. It was as though she had secretly been waiting all evening for this moment, for this invitation to walk along the beach with him. It scared her a little how much the prospect excited her.

Alexander took her hand and led her to the door that led out on to the path that wound down towards the beach. His grip felt sure and firm and sensuous. She loved the feel of his flesh against her flesh.

'Watch where you're going.' He kept a sharp eye on her, though the path was well lit and there was little fear of stumbling. And his care, his concern for her made her heart beat even faster. It was a new sensation—or one she had forgotten—this feeling of being looked after by a strong, tender man.

For there was tenderness in him, no doubt about that, Lisa reflected as they reached the foot of the path and headed across the rocky moonlit beach, his arm around her waist as though nothing could be more natural. There was tenderness, there was compassion, there was kindness, there was love, though obscured at times by the harder angles of his constantly changing Cancerian character.

She glanced up at the stars to avoid looking at his face. 'What a beautiful night. I've never seen so many stars.'

'We have many beautiful nights here.' He turned towards her as he said it. She felt for an instant the brush of his breath against her hair. 'Many beautiful nights that you are most welcome to share.'

The words fell on Lisa's ears, part statement, part invitation. She wondered for a moment if she was expected to answer. But, even as she wondered, she felt the arm at her waist tighten as, gently, he drew her round to face him.

She knew he would kiss her and her whole body was waiting for it, every nerve-end coiled in fierce anticipation as his free hand slid round to the back of her head, holding her there, as he looked down into her face.

'There really is no one else, you know.' He spoke the words softly. Almost a whisper. Almost a promise.

Then, as she nodded, believing him, her heart wildly rejoicing, with a soft sigh he was bending his head towards her, his fingers in her hair, his lips claiming hers.

Later Lisa was to wonder at the power of the sensations that swept in on her and possessed her at that moment. They were, if that was possible, even more ferocious than the first time he had kissed her. Like an explosion within her. Thunder and lightning. Like a pressure-cooker suddenly given release.

As his lips pressed against hers, warm and exciting, she could not hold back the longing inside her. Her arms twined around his neck, her body pressing against him, her lips receiving his with a passion that scorched her.

His hand was on her breast, moulding her flesh through her thin sweater, making her gasp and shudder softly as his palm grazed the taut nipple, tightening unbearably the ache within her. And the scent of him and the taste of him were making her giddy. She clung to him, every inch of her throbbing with desire.

'Lisa, my lovely Lisa.' He kissed her face, her ears, her throat. 'You taste of honey and wild strawberries and nectar. You taste of all the sweet things I've ever imagined.' Then he was seeking her lips again, plundering soft kisses, making her soul quake inside her, melting her bones.

'Lisa, sweet Lisa.' His tongue pricked against her tongue, exploring the sensitive inner reaches of her mouth. Then he was drawing back a little, his eyes washing over her. 'Say it,' he murmured. 'Say my name again. Say it, softly, the way you said it before.'

As Lisa looked back at him, heart racing, eyes barely focusing, she was aware of the intensity of emotion that sprang from him. For some reason it mattered to him that she should speak his name. For some reason he longed to hear it on her lips.

Her fingers touched his hair, smoothing its fine silkiness, running against his scalp, the back of his neck. She leaned forward and kissed him. 'Alexander,' she whispered. 'Alexander. The most beautiful name on earth.'

She felt a stab of emotion go driving through her. She had not meant to say that last part. It had sprung unbidden to her lips. But the moment she'd said it she'd realised she meant it. The knowledge left her shaken, gasping for breath.

Alexander's response would have left her breathless anyway. As the softly spoken syllables seemed to hover in the air around them with a soft moan he drew her fiercely against him, raining kisses on her face, making her shiver deliciously.

'The most beautiful thing on earth,' he told her huskily, 'is you.'

His mouth covered hers once more, masterful, demanding, drawing responses from within her that she had never before experienced. Her insides, it seemed, had turned to fire and water. Those two opposite and unmixable elements, that separately ruled herself and this man, were mixed now and flooding through her veins.

And then, quite unexpectedly, an earthquake shook her senses. As though the skin had been peeled from her aching nerve-ends, leaving them raw and unbearably sensitive.

He had slid one hand beneath the thin wool sweater, causing her skin to judder as he made contact with her naked midriff. Then in one easy movement his hand slid a little higher, his fingers deftly slipping the bra straps from her shoulders, then freeing her eager breasts from the lacy cups that imprisoned them.

As his palm cupped their heaviness, almost possessively, squeezing, caressing, make her blood leap, Lisa was suddenly overcome by a longing so intense that she had to restrain herself from falling on her knees and begging him to make love to her right there on the beach.

A sob escaped her lips. 'Alexander!' she moaned. Her body and mind were all at once throbbing with a barely suppressible aching need.

And it seemed he was intent on driving her crazy. Even as her senses swam out of focus from the sweet, cruel pleasure he was inflicting, he insisted on taking her one heartless step further. All at once, with a soft moan, he detached his lips from hers and, before she had realised what was happening, had bent to her breast to cover with his mouth, hungrily, one blood-gorged peak.

'Alexander! Oh, Alexander!' Her fingers were in his hair, unsure whether to encourage the fiery torment by pressing his face more firmly against her, or whether to end this excruciating torture by using her strength to drag him away.

In the end she did both. The fingers of one hand tugged and pulled, ineffectually, at the dark hair, while with the other hand she held him, her breast thrust against him, feeling the strength of her longing sap the power from her limbs.

By the time he had once more straightened, pulling her sweater down around her, kissing her, burying his face in her hair, she had to lean against him in order to remain upright. Her limbs trembled erratically, the muscles turned to jelly.

He framed her face in his hands and let his gaze pour over her. 'I asked you a question. You never answered.' He smiled at her, frowning. 'You will come back, won't you?'

Lisa felt an iridescent glow spread through her. A

sense of joy and delight and wonderment. She nodded.
'Of course I shall. I can think of nothing I want more.'

'That makes two of us.'

He held her against him for a moment. Then he was
smiling and laying a soft kiss against her lips before
slipping one strong arm around her shoulders and
leading her across the beach back to the house.

Sunday was another magical day.

Lisa had wondered uneasily when she'd awoken on
Sunday morning if what had passed between herself
and Alexander, on the beach beneath the moonlight,
the previous evening might cast an uncomfortable
shadow between them. In spite of the fact that he was
'as free as a bird', it was possible that he regretted what
had happened. That he might wish to forget it. That it
had merely been a lapse.

That possibility had caused a scurry of emotion inside
her, that, for the moment, Lisa had dared not examine
too closely. I'm being silly, it's not important, she had
told herself sternly as she had brushed her teeth before
hurrying down for breakfast. And she might have
accepted that but for the wry flicker in the eyes of the
reflection that had looked back at her from the bathroom mirror.

If it was so unimportant, why, last night, had she
scarcely slept for joy and excitement? Why had she
dreamed of Alexander and awakened with her mind
already full of bright thoughts of him? And why, right
now, did the thought of seeing him literally cause her
pulse to gallop?

She knew why, she told herself. It was sexual excitement—an element that had been missing from her life for too long. That was why she had reacted to him with such ferocity, why she had such difficulty tearing her mind away from him, why she shivered inside each time she pictured his face.

Once she had believed she could control these feelings, but in reality that was proving not so easy to do. And perhaps, she decided, being realistic, as long as she did not let things go too far it would do her no harm to stop trying to resist them and simply go with the flow of her feelings for a while. In time, like all corruptible passions of the flesh, this one would simply burn itself out.

In that sensible frame of mind she had hurried downstairs to join her daughter—who had beaten her to the breakfast table again!—and her host in the sunny conservatory.

Alexander had smiled and risen to his feet to kiss her lightly on the cheek. 'Come and join us. We were missing you,' he'd told her.

Had she been a little too pleased at his apparent pleasure at seeing her? At the fact that he had seemed to be regretting nothing? She tried to tell herself no, but throughout the day his smiles and glances, the way he touched her hand, were steadily, stealthily, wearing down her defences.

By Sunday evening, when it was time for them to leave and the three of them were piling into the Bentley, what she felt inside her, by any definition, was far more than simply sexual excitement. It was a yearning far more powerful than any yearning of the senses.

Yet she refused absolutely to recognise it, even when it jumped up and hit her in the face.

They were approaching Liskeard when Alexander suddenly turned to her. 'I'm afraid I won't be around next week.' His tone was detached. His eyes seemed to glide away from her. 'I have to go to London first thing tomorrow, and from there I have to fly to New York.'

He reached across and brushed the suddenly still hand in her lap. 'I'm really not sure when I'll be back.'

'Will you be back for the weekend?' She forced her voice to sound normal, though his cool words had felt like something driven against her heart.

'Probably not, though I'll be back for the following weekend. But my invitation stands. If you want to, please feel free to spend the weekend at Seaview.' His hand squeezed hers briefly, before returning to the steering-wheel. 'Urgent business matters. I hope you understand. I'm afraid I can't put them off any longer.'

'Of course I understand.'

She stared grimly ahead, carefully shutting herself off from the cold wind that suddenly blew around her heart.

Of course she understood. She understood perfectly. She knew what he was doing. She could take a hint.

For what better way to sever an unwanted tie than by disappearing off on business for a couple of weeks? It was clean, it was efficient, and yet it was subtle. It allowed both of them to retreat with their dignity intact.

And it didn't matter. It didn't matter in the slightest. It simply saved her the trouble of curbing her own foolish passions.

Back home, after Alexander had dropped them off and Emily was tucked up fast asleep in bed, Lisa even forced a smile of admiration at his duplicity. He had played his part so well throughout the day, holding her hand as they had strolled along the beach, looking into her eyes in that way that made her bones melt.

And it had all been an act, a ploy to save them both embarrassment after the mild indiscretions of the previous evening. Even the invitation to spend the weekend at Seaview; that had been as insincere as all the rest.

For he'd known she wouldn't go, that he was perfectly safe, that she was not the type to impose herself where she knew she wasn't wanted.

Tears sprang to her eyes then. Tears of anger. He had deceived her utterly from start to finish, and such calculated deceit was a downright insult!

Why had he insisted there was no one else when it was perfectly obvious that there was? And why had he felt the need to go on pretending right up until the very last minute?

Why couldn't he have had the decency just to be straight with her? Surely that was the very least she deserved? Was his vanity really so overpowering that he actually believed she gave a damn about him anyway?

Well, she didn't! He was wrong about that! She might have found him attractive, but there was no way in the world she could ever give a damn about a man who was as dishonest and as hard-hearted as he was!

And so, with her emotions wrapped up safely in a package of anger, Lisa proceeded to face the coming fortnight. She dared not think of Alexander. That would only distress her. So, instead, she concentrated on work.

And, work-wise, it proved to be a highly productive fortnight. Midway through the second week she had almost doubled the number of finished models that hung from the rails in the carefully locked cupboard.

And then on the morning of the second Thursday something happened that totally threw her.

Through her letter-box popped a postcard from New York, with on the front a picture of Lady Liberty, and on the back, in black ink, the simple message, 'Looking forward to seeing you soon. Lots of love, Alexander.'

Lisa stared at the message for a long, long time, trying to stifle the sudden swift beat of her heart.

Perhaps I've been wrong about him, after all! Perhaps there was no deception! She actually dared to think it.

And suddenly the emotions that went tearing through her were so terrifying, so cataclysmic, that she had to thrust them from her. If she *had* been wrong about him. . .? If he had *not* deceived her. . .? At the thought she felt her heart unfold with joy within her.

Then she stopped herself short. And if she had *not* been mistaken. . .? If this postcard was simply another of his callous deceptions. . .?

Then it did not matter. It really did not matter. Over and over she repeated that conviction, her mind clinging to it stubbornly, knowing it was her salvation. Were she to believe that it did matter, she would be finished.

Somehow, with gritted teeth, her soul in torment, she got through the day and the night that followed.

Next morning, for the first time since she had started at G.W., she arrived late, almost too terrified to step across the threshold. This was the day, his secretary had told her, that Alexander was due back.

It was just gone eleven when, passing by her desk, Leo advised her casually, 'Vass is back. He wants to see you.'

Lisa's heart stopped inside her. Just for a moment she felt paralysed, as though she were bolted to her seat. Then something burst inside her, flooding through her. She could not hold it back. She leapt to her feet.

The next instant, dizzy with the excitement that possessed her, she was hurrying along the corridor towards his office.

The door was ajar. She pushed it open, joy and anticipation lighting up her face.

'Alexander. . .!' she began.

Then she stopped dead in her tracks, the blood seeping from her veins, leaving her stiff and white with shock.

For, though Alexander was there, he was clearly not expecting her to walk in on him at that precise moment. He was standing by his desk, his arms circling the waist of an extraordinarily beautiful dark-haired girl, who was looking back at Lisa in surprise across his shoulder.

Lisa recognised her instantly. It was Nina.

CHAPTER ELEVEN

LISA's instant reaction was to back out of the door again. 'I'm sorry,' she stammered. 'Please excuse me.' She felt sick to her soul and numb with misery. What a fool she had been. What a daydreaming idiot!

'No need to excuse yourself.' As she stumbled back into the corridor Alexander disengaged himself from the embrace of the dark-haired woman. 'Come in,' he invited Lisa. 'Come in and meet Nina.'

The only thing Lisa wanted to do was flee, but she summoned the strength from somewhere to step back into the office, pinning a brave smile to her face. Like an automaton, she held out her hand to Nina. 'How do you do? I'm Lisa Howell,' she heard herself say.

'Lisa's our brilliant new designer. The one I've been telling you all about.' As Lisa briefly grasped cool manicured fingers Alexander moved closer to the dark-haired girl's side. His hand was on her waist, Lisa noticed in stiff misery, a gesture of easy, affectionate familiarity.

'I've been dying to meet you.' Nina was quite stunning. A perfect oval face, thick, glossy hair and the same bright sparkle in the wide brown eyes that had been so evident in the photograph at Seaview. And she was Greek. That was clear from the soft, seductive accent. Which made her, all in all, Lisa decided with bitter anguish, the perfect partner for Alexander.

168

She had a sudden cruel memory of his false denial, 'There really is no one else, you know.' She felt shame wash through her. She had never wholly believed it, but oh, how desperately she had wanted to!

She glanced up at him now, fighting for composure, as he said to her, 'Nina's dying to have a look at the new collections. Perhaps, if you have a moment, you wouldn't mind showing her?'

'Of course. I'd be delighted.' It was an effort to keep smiling. The muscles in her face felt stiff and frozen. 'Any time you like. Just say the word.'

'Good. Oh, by the way, Nina and I——' As he spoke the flicker of a smile crossed his eyes. But he was destined never to finish the sentence. At that very moment a wild-eyed Leo appeared in the office doorway behind Lisa.

'Lisa! Mr Vass! Something terrible has happened. The models. . .they've all gone! The cupboard is empty!'

With Leo's announcement the world went crazy. The next instant everyone was talking at once.

'Gone? What's happened to them?'

'They must have been stolen.'

'It must have been last night!'

'But how could it have happened?'

'Never mind how it could have happened. Someone get on to the police immediately!'

Then, with Alexander leading the way, Lisa and Leo were hurrying along the corridor to the pillaged cupboard. The door stood open and the rails stood empty. Every single one of the models had gone.

Lisa remembered staring blankly, in weak disbelief. Once she could not have imagined a greater disaster—all the garments she'd been working on, with such dedication, day and night, for weeks on end now, had totally vanished, disappeared. Surely nothing in the world could be more tragic than that?

But to her heart, already sore and aching from Alexander, this new blow, by comparison, seemed a mere trifle. She still had the designs. She could remake all the garments. It would half kill her, but at least a remedy existed.

In a kind of distracted daze, she stood on the sidelines as the police arrived and started asking questions. As best she could she answered the ones they put to her, but that was the extent of her participation. She felt oddly detached from the comings and goings all around her. All she wanted was to escape and be on her own. Finally to let her mind slip free of all this chaos, turn her face to the wall and weep slow tears.

She was vaguely aware at one stage in the proceedings of Alexander, with Nina hovering at his elbow, standing in a huddle with a tall plain-clothes detective. She was no more needed, she realised wretchedly, than she wanted to be here.

It was mid-afternoon when Alexander informed the staff, 'You can all go home now. Thanks for all your help.' Then he and Nina and the detective inspector were hurrying from the building and climbing into an unmarked police car.

Pale-cheeked, Lisa watched till the car disappeared from sight, then she gathered up her things and quietly left the office.

She moved like a sleep-walker, her heart ship-wrecked within her. The only thing that held her together was her skin.

Josey helped her through the evening.

'As soon as you stepped out of the car I knew something was wrong,' her friend confided later over a cup of tea. 'And, even when you told me about the break-in, I knew it wasn't really that.' She squeezed Lisa's arm and frowned into her pale face. 'I'm so sorry about Alexander,' she murmured.

Lisa's fingers were wrapped around her teacup as she sat by the gas fire, staring into it. 'It's my own fault. I knew what kind of man he was.' As she spoke her knuckles tightened into shiny pebbles. 'Oh, Josey, what an absolute idiot I've been!'

Tears scalded her eyes. She blinked them back hurriedly and forced herself to look across at Josey. 'Thanks for taking Emily off my hands this evening. You really are the best friend a person could ever have.'

Josey squeezed her arm again. 'Think nothing of it. I could see you needed some time by yourself. And besides,' she added, 'Emily's no bother. It was a pleasure having her round to tea.'

Lisa swallowed. 'I'm grateful all the same.' She let her eyes stray for a moment to the door of the bedroom where her little daughter now lay fast asleep. Then she shifted her gaze, frowning, back to the gas fire. 'I don't know what got into me. I just fell apart.'

'I'm not surprised.' Josey's tone was firm and kindly. 'Since this morning you've had two huge shocks to your system. And you didn't fall apart. You just looked as though you might. And who on earth could blame you for that?'

A wry smile touched Lisa's lips. Had she played her part so convincingly? Had she really managed to look as though she were still holding together? One look inside her at the devastation of her soul would have told a very different story.

She stared into the flames, almost speaking to herself. 'The thing is, it's been building up inside me for weeks. I've been trying to ignore it—scared to face it—trying to pretend I didn't care.

'You see, I know how I am. In love I don't hold back. If I'd admitted to myself how I really felt about him I'd have thrown myself into the whole thing, body and soul. And I knew that would be folly. I knew I couldn't trust him. . .'

Her voice trailed off a moment, then she took a deep breath. 'But when that postcard arrived, that ridiculous postcard, with that ridiculous message that didn't mean a thing, I thought. . .' Her voice faltered. 'I thought. . .' She shook her head. 'Oh, Josey,' she sighed, 'what an idiot I've been!'

Josey was watching her from the other side of the fireplace. 'There's nothing idiotic about falling in love.'

'There is when the man you choose to fall in love with is as false and unscrupulous as Alexander Vass!'

There was hurt and real anger in her voice, but, beneath all that, there was tenderness, too. She *did* love Alexander, deeply and passionately, and suddenly it seemed quite natural to say so, in spite of the fact that it was only so recently that she had dared to look her love in the face.

She had finally confronted the truth this morning when Leo had told her, unaware of the news's import, 'Vass is back. He wants to see you.' The explosion of joy that had suddenly burst through her at the thought of seeing him, at the thought of being with him, for a moment had overcome her senses.

And that charge of excitement and tenderness and longing, she had realised instantly, was not, as she had tried to tell herself, purely physical in origin. It had burst out of her heart, out of the very depths of her being. It was love, so real that she could have held it in her hand.

But, even as she remembered that wonderful moment, another, crueller memory came rushing over her. That moment when she had stepped through his office doorway and seen him standing there with Nina. The pain that crushed against her heart was unbearable.

Lisa stared hard into the fire as despair flooded through her, then, fighting for control, she raised her cup to her lips and forced herself to drink a mouthful of warm tea. What good was this love that she should never have given birth to? She must kill it, at once, before it could destroy her.

She breathed for a moment, slowly, then said to Josey, 'I'm all right now. If you want to go home, please don't feel you have to stay.'

Josey looked back at her in silence, then she reached across and touched her, causing the tears to fly once more to Lisa's eyes. 'Keep you chin up,' she said softly.

'And remember what you said earlier—after the way he lied to you, he's not worth loving.'

Lisa nodded, swallowing, wishing she could believe that with her heart as she believed it with her head. She laid down her teacup. 'Thanks again, Josey.' Then she stood up and led her friend to the door.

'Try to get some sleep. I'll see you tomorrow.' As Lisa pulled the door open Josey stepped out into the night. . .and literally came within a hair's breadth of walking straight into the tall dark figure who was striding up the path.

'I beg your pardon!'

As Alexander stood aside, glancing apologetically at Josey, Lisa stared at him, dumbstruck, wondering if she was dreaming. Then she noticed the black Bentley parked outside the gate. This was no dream. It was horribly real.

Lisa was vaguely aware of a wide-eyed Josey hurrying down the path, heading for her own house, but it was the tall figure in the grey suit that commanded all her attention. Through the turmoil in her heart, she demanded, 'What do you want?'

'A word.' He stood before her in the doorway, evidently expecting to be invited in.

But a confrontation with him now was more than Lisa could handle. She stood firm, blocking the entrance. 'I'm sorry. Some other time.'

She'd half expected him to barge past her, just like that other time, and she'd resolved to set about him with her fists if he tried. But he did not mow her down. He stood there on the doorstep. 'I think you want to hear what I have to say,' he told her. 'There are a couple of things I need to put straight between us.'

'Like what?' She tried to quell the commotion in her heart. Hope and fear were tripping over each other inside her.

'Let me in and I'll tell you. We can't discuss things here. Surely you wouldn't want such very personal business to be made public out here on the doorstep?'

Lisa was fearful still, her heart beating erratically. What was he saying? Dared she trust him? She looked into his eyes, into their endless blackness, seeking silent reassurance that he would inflict no more pain. And there was a glimmer of something, enough to persuade her to stand reluctantly aside and murmur, 'You'd better come in.'

In silent single file they walked down the narrow corridor, Lisa staring at his back through eyes that were barely focused. With all her heart she was fearing that she might regret this decision.

In the sitting-room doorway, Alexander turned to look at her. 'I brought this.' He smiled and drew from his pocket a silver hip-flask. 'Brandy,' he told her. 'I could do with a shot and I know you don't keep any in the house. Will you join me? There's more than enough here for two.'

Lisa was about to say no, but then she thought better of it. A shot of brandy might soothe her twanging nerves. She nodded curtly. 'Very well. I'll get some glasses.'

But he was striding ahead of her into the kitchen. 'Don't worry, I remember where they're kept.'

By the time he came back into the sitting-room,

carrying a couple of tumblers, Lisa had seated herself nervously in one of the armchairs. She watched as he sat opposite her on the worn old sofa and proceeded to pour the brandy into the glasses. Heaven help me, she prayed silently. What have I let myself in for?

As he handed her one of the glasses their eyes met briefly, and it occurred to Lisa, for just a fleeting instant, that he was feeling almost as nervous as she was. But she rejected the notion as he leaned back against the cushions and took a quick swig of his brandy. What could Alexander possibly have to feel nervous about?

And, as their eyes met again, she could see that she was right. There was no hint of any emotion even distantly related to nervousness in those dark, intelligent, ruthless eyes.

He said, 'First the good news. We've got all the garments back.'

'All of them? Really?' She half smiled. 'That's wonderful.' What did he mean, 'First the good news'? she wondered, her heart shrinking.

'I thought you'd be pleased.' He laid down his drink. 'What's more, they're undamaged. A little crumpled, but no more than that.' He smiled. 'I suppose you'd like me to tell you where we found them?'

'Of course.' She feigned enthusiasm, but what she was really thinking was that she'd been a fool to hope he'd come here on a more personal mission. She ought to have known that only matters of business would have brought him to her door.

But he was oblivious of her pain. He continued with his story. 'We found them at the home of Nigel, your predecessor. And the only reason that they were undamaged was because he hadn't made up his mind whether simply to destroy them, his original intention, or whether to try to sell the designs to someone else. As always, his greed got tangled up with his malice.'

Lisa was frowning, listening now with sudden interest. 'Nigel, you say? What made you suspect that he was behind it?'

Alexander leaned back against the cushions. 'I'm afraid poor old Nigel was responsible for everything.'

'Everything?'

'Everything.'

'Even the fire? I thought you said that wasn't possible? I remember you telling me that on the night of the fire he was at the pub with a group of friends.'

'So he was. But his accomplice wasn't.' Alexander smiled grimly. 'Kerry, to be precise.'

'Kerry? My design assistant?' Lisa blinked at him and sat forward, frowning, in her chair. 'You mean all this time Kerry's been working against you?' She shook her head and let out a gasp of bewilderment. 'You're going to have to explain what on earth's been going on!'

A smile touched his lips. 'I'll be only too glad to. I think you of all people deserve an explanation.' His eyes fastened with hers a moment, causing a shiver to go through her. Then he sighed. 'OK. Let's start at the beginning. . .'

He began by telling her about his bid for G.W. Fashions and the antagonism it had sparked among his rivals. One firm in particular had proved a very bad

loser, making certain hostile comments about him to
the Press.

'I think that may have been what gave Nigel the idea
of starting his little campaign against me. At any rate,
he didn't waste any time. The ink was scarcely dry on
the takeover agreement when he made his first inept
move against me. . .

'Of course, I had no idea it was Nigel who was
responsible. All I knew was that one afternoon while I
was at the office in London someone poured petrol
through my letter-box at Seaview, along with a note
warning me that if I didn't get out of G.W. Fashions
there would be other similarly unpleasant incidents to
look forward to, and that next time the petrol would
be accompanied by a lighted rag.'

He paused a moment. 'It was the very next day that
you so inconveniently smashed up my car——'

'So you jumped to the conclusion that the two
episodes were connected and instantly assumed that
the villain was me!'

'It was a natural assumption.' He smiled. 'But I
apologise. Besides, it didn't take me long to figure out
I was wrong.'

'So why did you accuse me of starting the fire at the
factory? That doesn't sound like an act of trust to me!'

'You're right, it doesn't.' Alexander sipped his drink
and watched her over the rim of his glass as he
continued. 'After your arrival I received another
anonymous letter, informing me that you had been
planted by my enemies. Its purpose, I suppose, was
simply to unnerve me, but, though I didn't believe it, I

felt unable to dismiss it. There were too many strange things happening around me at the time.'

Lisa nodded in sympathy. It couldn't have been easy. Then she frowned and queried, 'But why did Nigel want rid of you? Why was he prepared to go to all that trouble?'

'Lots of reasons, the main one being that he was basically a crook with a number of little operations going at the factory. He was a chronic thief. Bits of machinery and bales of fabric kept mysteriously disappearing. And I was a new broom with a reputation for sweeping clean. He knew that, if I stayed, his thieving days were done.'

'Is that why you got rid of him—because you found out what he was up to?' Lisa felt a warm sensation of relief creep through her. At last, here was the explanation she had secretly longed for, the proof that he was not the ruthless, uncaring employer, after all.

Alexander nodded. 'Yes, you could say that. I suspected about his thieving, but I couldn't prove it at that stage. Then, quite by chance, I caught him red-handed, stealing the wallet of one of the machinists out of the cloakroom. He said he'd go quietly if I didn't make it public, and I agreed. As I said, I'd no idea he was the one who was threatening me and I simply thought I was well shot of him, quite frankly.'

Lisa frowned. 'I expect he was planning to get his job back once he'd managed to get rid of you. . .'

'My suspicions exactly.'

'So what happened next?'

Alexander ran a hand across his dark hair, that soft springy hair that Lisa's own fingers had once touched.

Something flared inside her, but she quickly quelled it and forced herself to concentrate on what he was saying.

'Well, in fact, there was a great deal happening, it transpires. Our friend Nigel had anonymously contacted the company who had made the fuss about the takeover, telling them about his little campaign and inviting them to offer their financial support.'

'What an absolute nerve!'

'More like absolute folly. Needless to say, they went straight to the police, just as I'd done when I received that first threat. I won't go into details, but with the two letters at their disposal, plus a couple of other bits of evidence, the forensic people had a field-day. Apparently they were literally poised to arrest both Nigel and Kerry when the clothes were found to be missing from the cupboard this morning. It meant they knew exactly where to go looking for them.'

Lisa nodded. Was it really just this morning that it had all happened? She felt a splinter of pain awaken in her heart and a sense of grief go rushing through her. Nina, she remembered. The memory numbed her. She said through her agony, 'Fancy Kerry being involved in this. She wasn't very friendly, but I never suspected she was evil.'

'As much weak as evil, I suspect,' said Alexander. 'Apparently no one knew about her relationship with Nigel—after all, Nigel's a married man. But it appears she was totally under his influence. She would have done anything he told her. And she did. She started the fire at the factory.'

'Poor, foolish girl.' Lisa shook her head. Then she

sat back and sighed. 'So, at last it's all over. You must be feeling pretty relieved.'

'I'm relieved, all right. It's been a bit of a nightmare.' He threw her a smile. 'I'm sorry you got involved. I apologise for any upset it's caused you.'

'No need to apologise. I understand now. Though at the time,' she added with a wry shake of her head, 'it was something of a novelty to be accused of being a criminal.'

'It won't happen again.' He was smiling across at her. Then he leaned towards her, an odd expression on his face. 'I guess that's more or less everything sorted out.'

'I guess it is.' Her heartbeat faltered. She sensed she did not want to hear anything else.

But he was about to say something. Quickly Lisa jumped in, putting to him a question she had always wondered about. 'Why did you insist that I go to work for you. . .? When you knew about my plans to start my own business. . .? I've always thought that was a little hard-hearted of you.'

He had not moved. Elbows on knees, his expression intent, Alexander continued to lean towards her. 'Hard-hearted? I hope not.' He sighed and elaborated, 'Though I suppose my reasons were partly selfish. I needed a new designer and I had a very strong instinct that you were precisely what I was looking for.

'But it wasn't simply that. I was afraid for you, Lisa. I think I even told you that at one point. I was afraid you mightn't make it on your own.'

Yes, he had told her, and she had not believed him. She was still not certain that she believed him now.

'Why did you think I might fail? If I was good enough to employ, surely I was also good enough to make it on my own?'

'You could be right. But I had this instinct that you'd have a better chance if you first spent some time with me——'

'Under your guidance?' There was an edge to the question. She felt vulnerable, afraid he was not being sincere.

But the dark eyes that looked back at her were firm and steady. 'Precisely that. Under my guidance. And I was right, was I not? We work well together.'

Lisa's heart felt like a huge fist clenched in her chest, so tight, so hard, that she could scarcely breathe. 'I suppose so,' she said. Then, almost angrily, she asked him, 'Why should I believe that you were afraid for me? You make it sound as though you cared about my welfare!'

'I did. I do. Do you doubt it?' All at once, in one quick movement, he'd taken hold of her hand and, rising to his feet, was drawing her with him. His free hand was on her waist. His lips brushed against her hair. 'Surely, my dear Lisa, you cannot doubt it?'

Quite involuntarily Lisa gasped, the sound almost a cry of anguish. His flesh burned into her. She could not bear the sweet pain of it.

She heard herself say, 'You seem to be forgetting about Nina. I doubt very much that she would approve of this.'

'Nina. . .Ah, yes. . .I was forgetting. . .' He drew back a little and looked into her face, though Lisa had not the strength to meet his gaze. 'Nina. . .That's the other thing I have to tell you. . .'

The clenched fist inside her seemed to press against her rib-cage. Lisa opened her mouth to silence his confession, but no sound came out. She could not speak.

He was drawing out her torture, one hand against her cheek now, caressing her skin softly, making her blood burn. 'Nina. . .' he said softly. 'Let me clarify the position. Nina, my dear Lisa, as you ought to have guessed. . .is not my girlfriend. She is my cousin.'

Lisa felt the colour ebb and flow in her face. 'Cousin?' she echoed foolishly. 'Nina's your cousin?'

'She's the cousin I once told you about. The one who lost her husband. The one who I told you used to keep running to me for help.' He tilted her chin so she was forced to look at him. 'But she won't be running to me any more. She's just got engaged. She's about to be married. That's the news she came here to tell me.'

There was a second of silence, the air holding its breath.

'I hope,' said Alexander, frowning down at her, 'that you're pleased to hear that particular piece of news?'

'Oh, yes. Very pleased.' Her heart expanded. 'Very, very pleased indeed.'

He kissed her forehead. 'There's something else.'

Lisa looked at him. The blood in her veins had stopped flowing.

Then he kissed her lips softly, drawing her against him. 'I love you,' he told her. 'I love you and I want to marry you.'

The darkness that had possessed her at once scattered into light, and the joy that replaced it was too powerful to contain. Lisa threw back her head and let out a peal of happiness.

'Oh, yes!' She flung her arms around his neck, all the passion of her fiery Arien nature in her eyes. 'I love you, Alexander! Of course I'll be your wife!'

Just over one month later they took the fashion world by storm.

At the end of the first public showing of her new collections Lisa was obliged by the uproar of cheering from the crowd to step out on stage and take a bow.

There were tears in her eyes as she looked down across the footlights to the man in the front row, on his feet now, applauding. She threw him a kiss as he winked up at her, smiling.

'Thank you!' she called out to him over the hubbub. Thank you for everything, she added in her heart. Thank you for being my guide and my inspiration, for being a wonderful father to my little girl and, above all, thank you for being the best husband in the world.

And through all the commotion of clapping and cheering, just for a moment, the world stood still.

Their eyes met.

He smiled.

And Lisa's heart brimmed over as, with a look of adoration, Alexander responded with the words she never tired of hearing. A brief and simple message. 'Darling, I love you.'

STARGAZING

YOUR STAR SIGN: **CANCER (June 22–July 23)**

CANCER is the first of the Water signs, ruled by the Moon and controlled by the element of Earth. These combinations tend to make you extremely sensitive even though you may appear tough and protected by your crab-like shell! While you are generous and kind, others should be wary as you always expect something in return!

Socially, you tend to prefer several close relationships and you love taking care of things and people. At home you can be loving, indulgent and forgiving most of the time but friends should beware—you hate any sort of intrusion or disruption in your life.

Your characteristics in love: Cancerians are the great romantics—highly emotional and soft-hearted, you are not one for light-hearted flirtations! But partners should beware—you are often afraid of being hurt and your natural defence mechanism means loved ones must always be careful about what they say! None the less, your natural affection and loyalty means that people are attracted to you—you are never likely to be short of romance in your life!

Signs which are compatible with you: **Scorpio**, **Pisces**, **Taurus** and **Virgo**, are the most harmonious, while you may well have met your match if you choose **Capricorn**, **Aries** or **Libra** as your partner! Other signs can also be compatible, depending on which planets reside in their Houses of Personality and Romance.

What is your star-career? Cancerians love to take care of people or animals and have a natural potential to be good nurses, doctors, social workers, teachers and therapists—in fact, any job which involves looking after others! Positions which involve talking to people will also appeal to you—child care, personal management, banking or writing will bring out your natural ability for communication.

Your colours and birthstones: As your sign is ruled by the Moon, there is little surprise in knowing that your birthstones are moonstone and pearl, whose milky hues both indicate the Moon's influence over your life. The ocean pearl was once regarded by ancient astrologers as a symbol of chastity and purity but was also thought to encourage greed. Cancerians, with their influences of the Earth and Moon, tend to go for pale colours which you will find have a calming and soothing influence over your life!

CANCER ASTRO-FACTFILE

Day of the week: Monday
Countries: New Zealand and Holland
Flowers: Marigolds, water-lily and wild flowers
Food: Pears, white fish; Cancerians make wonderful cooks and are excellent home-makers. They enjoy preparing food such as creamy dishes for others but do themselves have a tendency to overeat!
Health: Be careful not to let upsets get the better of you or you will be plagued with digestive problems! The ribs, sternum and digestive organs are often sensitive so beware of heartburn and gastric disorders which can happen when someone upsets a Cancerian's sensitive nature. Lots of friends, sensible eating and emotional happiness are the key to your overall well-being.

You share your star sign with these famous names:

The Princess of Wales   Tom Cruise
Esther Rantzen   Ringo Starr
Meryl Streep   Harrison Ford
Daley Thompson   Wayne Sleep

Next Month's Romances

Each month you can choose from a world of variety in romance with Mills & Boon. Below are the new titles to look out for next month, why not ask either Mills & Boon Reader Service or your Newsagent to reserve you a copy of the titles you want to buy — just tick the titles you would like to order and either post to Reader Service or take it to any Newsagent and ask them to order your books.

Please save me the following titles:	Please tick	√
STORMFIRE	Helen Bianchin	
LAW OF ATTRACTION	Penny Jordan	
DANGEROUS SANCTUARY	Anne Mather	
ROMANTIC ENCOUNTER	Betty Neels	
A DARING PROPOSITION	Miranda Lee	
NO PROVOCATION	Sophie Weston	
LAST OF THE GREAT FRENCH LOVERS	Sarah Holland	
CAVE OF FIRE	Rebecca King	
NO MISTRESS BUT LOVE	Kate Proctor	
INTRIGUE	Margaret Mayo	
ONE LOVE FOREVER	Barbara McMahon	
DOUBLE FIRE	Mary Lyons	
STONE ANGEL	Helen Brooks	
THE ORCHARD KING	Miriam Macgregor	
LAW OF THE CIRCLE	Rosalie Ash	
THE HOUSE ON CHARTRES STREET	Rosemary Hammond	

If you would like to order these books from Mills & Boon Reader Service please send £1.70 per title to: Mills & Boon Reader Service, P.O. Box 236, Croydon, Surrey, CR9 3RU and quote your Subscriber No:...(If applicable) and complete the name and address details below. Alternatively, these books are available from many local Newsagents including W.H.Smith, J.Menzies, Martins and other paperback stockists from 6th July 1992.

Name:...

Address:...

....Post Code:.......................

To Retailer: If you would like to stock M&B books please contact your regular book/magazine wholesaler for details.

You may be mailed with offers from other reputable companies as a result of this application. If you would rather not take advantage of these opportunities please tick box ☐

4 FREE

Romances
and 2 FREE gifts
just for you!

*You can enjoy all the
heartwarming emotion of true love for FREE!
Discover the heartbreak and the happiness, the emotion and
the tenderness of the modern relationships in
Mills & Boon Romances.*

*We'll send you 4 captivating Romances as a special offer from
Mills & Boon Reader Service, along with the chance to have
6 Romances delivered to your door each month.*

Claim your FREE books and gifts overleaf...

An irresistible offer from Mills & Boon

Here's a personal invitation from Mills & Boon Reader Service, to become a regular reader of Romances. To welcome you, we'd like you to have 4 books, a CUDDLY TEDDY and a special MYSTERY GIFT absolutely FREE.

Then you could look forward each month to receiving 6 brand new Romances, delivered to your door, postage and packing free! Plus our free Newsletter featuring author news, competitions, special offers and much more.

This invitation comes with no strings attached. You may cancel or suspend your subscription at any time, and still keep your free books and gifts.

It's so easy. Send no money now. Simply fill in the coupon below and post it to -
Reader Service, FREEPOST, PO Box 236, Croydon, Surrey CR9 9EL.

- - - - - - - - - - - - NO STAMP REQUIRED - - - - - - - - - -

Free Books Coupon

Yes! Please rush me 4 free Romances and 2 free gifts! Please also reserve me a Reader Service subscription. If I decide to subscribe I can look forward to receiving 6 brand new Romances each month for just £10.20, postage and packing free. If I choose not to subscribe I shall write to you within 10 days - I can keep the books and gifts whatever I decide. I may cancel or suspend my subscription at any time. I am over 18 years of age.

Ms/Mrs/Miss/Mr_____ EP31R

Address _____

_____

Postcode_____Signature _____

Offer expires 31st May 1993. The right is reserved to refuse an application and change the terms of this offer. Readers overseas and in Eire please send for details. Southern Africa write to Book Services International Ltd, P.O. Box 42654, Craighall, Transvaal 2024. You may be mailed with offers from other reputable companies as a result of this application.
If you would prefer not to share in this opportunity, please tick box ☐